Hi Sex Enjoy!

THRIVING IN SEX WORK
WORKBOOK

WRITTEN BY LOLA DAVINA

ILLUSTRATED BY FELICIA GOTTHELF

xo ox Lola D.

THE EROTIC AS POWER PRESS
OAKLAND CALIFORNIA

Hi Sexy -
Enjoy!

♥ ♥

xo

Published by:
The Erotic as Power Press LLC
248 3rd St. #646
Oakland, CA 94607

Cover design by Albert Ochosa | Sun Rising Media
Interior design and layout by Rob Siders | 52 Novels
Illustrations and copyedit by Felicia Gotthelf
Back cover author photo by Lisa Keating Photography

Note on front cover:
Images are stock photos posed by models, for illustrative purpose only.

Library of Congress Cataloging-in-Publication Data
Davina, Lola, 1968–
Gotthelf, Felicia, 1970–

Thriving in sex work workbook/ by Lola Davina and Felicia Gotthelf
p. cm.
Includes bibliographical references.
ISBN 978-0-9988920-9-2 1. Sex work 2. Self-care

Our visions begin with our desires.

AUDRE LORDE

We write in order to change the world.

JAMES BALDWIN

CONTENTS

Introduction

INTRODUCTION

Hi Sexy—

Sex work doesn't come with a beginner's manual. Some sex workers are lucky to have help getting started in the Biz; others meet fellow travelers along the way. But when it comes right down to the nitty-gritty, no one else can guide us. In sex work, we figure 99% of the job out on our own.

There are systemic reasons for this, including the stigma, criminalization, and exploitation that goes along with any marginalized occupation. But one major contributing factor to our isolation is inherent to the job and yet not a result of oppression: sexuality is fundamentally mysterious. From the earliest age, we're taught a vast array of mixed messages about what is sacred, what is disgusting, what is intoxicating, what is taboo. We learn to be sexual in secret, figuring out our bodies late at night, under the covers in the dark. We explore each other in real life, groping in the backseats of cars, at an age when our bodies, brains, and personalities aren't yet fully developed. The Internet offers billions of sexual images ranging from the dazzling to the depraved, usually stripped of context, and devoid of any interest in mutual pleasure. Even when grown, even after years of practice, for many of us sexuality remains dark and tangled. A terrain that promises pleasure and danger in equal measure, where language, logic, linearity, restraint, self-possession, and morality break down and leave us.

As if all that isn't complicated enough, money is thrown into the mix, which can be just as emotionally charged as sex. Each job title brings its own challenges: while certain dynamics are similar, phone sex will never be the same as stripping. There is just no way to make generalized statements that hold true for everyone, which is why I don't believe anyone will be writing *Sex Work For Dummies* anytime soon.

That doesn't mean, however, that we can't make any kind of sense out of this wacky industry. Other people's advice is lovely, but it's not required **to know what we already know.** For those us who have done the work for a while, we do have the power to explain the job to ourselves.

The purpose of this workbook is just that: providing a framework, a conceptual structure to answer these three questions:

1. What does sex work mean for me now?
2. How do I cultivate my life, including sex work, to be safe, happy, and nurturing?
3. What do I want for myself in the future?

Hopefully, Sexy Reader, as a bonus, we can have some fun along the way. ☺

THRIVING IN SEX WORK CHECKLIST

As a refresher, here's the *Thriving in Sex Work* checklist. I've provided space to take extended notes on pages 134-145 of this workbook. This is where we're headed together.

As you read these over, check in with how they make you feel. Do any of these feel unimportant, out of reach, or like they don't apply to you? Do you know why you might feel that way? Don't worry if you don't have everything all figured out right now. This book is designed to help you take affirmative, practical steps towards success in sex work on every level of your life.

YOU ARE TRULY THRIVING IN SEX WORK WHEN:

1. **You love yourself, you love your life.**

2. **You take care of your health and have interest in physical pleasure.**

3. **You have time and energy for outside interests.**

4. **You have love in your life, including friends, family, coworkers, pets, and/or romantic partners, and a sense of community.**

5. **You have a personal support network that gets you and your decision to be a sex worker.**

6. **You have a professional support network.**

7. **Your clients provide you with the money and gratification you deserve.**

8. **You understand, have weighed, and made conscious decisions about the risks you take.**

9. **You have a financial plan.**

10. **You choose to do sex work.**

11. **Sex work exceeds your expectations, and your life is better than when you started.**

How to Use This Workbook

You're free to use this workbook however you like, of course. Skip around, tear pages out, scribble the answers in your journal or on your iPad or in crayon on the walls. Workbooks are intended to be creative, engaging, and fun.

That being said, however, these exercises are serious business. If you consider sex work to be a real job, treat it like one. I strongly recommend that you:

1. **Actively interact with the material.** So many times I find myself nodding "yes, yes, yes" when reading an advice book, but as soon as I put it down, I'm done. When learning about somebody else's story, it's fine to let knowledge wash over you. To make change in *your* life, you must engage.

2. **Write/draw out your answers rather than answering only in your mind.** The more you put into it, the more you'll get out of it—the act of writing is an act of thinking, the first step necessary for doing. Research shows that jotting down words and phrases assists in both comprehension and memory retention. You also have something to refer back to later, and sometimes that can be the sweetest gift. A message in a bottle, sent to yourself.

3. **Consider your audience.** Perhaps you give your best answers when speaking directly to yourself, but often we communicate better when challenged by someone else. Imagine how you might explain this crazy thing called "sex work" to your best friend. Debate it with your worst enemy. Break it down into bite-sized nuggets for a stranger who knows nothing about the job.

4. **Be systematic.** There is a lot of homework here—rushing isn't much better than not doing it at all. Address one page at a time, and fill it out completely. Any questions that don't pertain to you, cross them out—don't leave them blank. Give yourself the satisfaction of working every day towards your goals.

5. **Hold yourself accountable.** It's easy and fun to do easy and fun things, but the crux of self-discovery comes from doing hard, scary stuff—this is where change is born. If you're tempted to skip a page or an exercise, ask yourself why: is it really because it doesn't apply to you, or because it feels too hard right now? If you need to take a break, that's okay, but make a promise to yourself to come back and address what you don't get done today.

6. **Get some support, if possible.** Set up a book circle with your working buddies and meet once or twice a month to discuss your progress. Sharing your hopes and dreams with other people brings them to life.

7. Let me take a moment, however, to make a special plea: **Be careful about what you share online.** Discretion is the better part of valor in sex work—and in social media. When dealing with serious matters here in the real world, stop for a minute and think through the consequences before you post your most intimate thoughts in the virtual world.

WORKBOOK STRUCTURE

Think of working this book like setting off on an adventure. This workbook is laid out to help you every step along the way.

Sex Work Safety 101

Imagine this first section as basic travel preparation before ever leaving the house—stock up your first-aid kit, put gas in the tank and air in the tires. **Do these first.**

Creating My Bright Future

Half the fun of a trip is plotting your course. This is where we fantasize about becoming the sex worker we would like to become, and write fan letters to our sex work hero/ines. We use our tools—creativity, intentionality, and vision work—to tap into deep erotics and conjure up what we love in order to attract more of it. **Do these in order after completing *Sex Work Safety 101*.**

Taking Care of Business

Next, we put those visions to work. Here we declare what kind of clientele we want, what our rules and boundaries are. We prepare a monthly budget, manage our schedule, and identify our core motivations. We plan ahead to take care of business during slowdown periods. Additionally, self-care action plans ought to be mandatory in sex work; you'll find them here. **Do these in order after completing *Creating My Bright Future*.**

Slaying Demons

Along the path, we'll be tested in new ways, and may find old patterns don't work for us anymore. Think of *Slaying Demons* as a travel toolbox full of exercises and practices to address envy, shame, anger, sadness, and the rest. You may want to work on these exercises in order, as negative emotions flare up in your daily life, or in tandem with other sections. You'll get the most out of them when the material feels alive and relevant. **As needed.**

Extra Help

We all face rough patches such as experiencing panic attacks, dealing with difficult clients and coworkers, and getting outed. *Extra Help* is an emergency kit providing resources and exercises to get you through hard times. **As needed.**

Thriving in Sex Work Checklist Revisited

Here's where we keep track of our progress. In the back of this workbook are the eleven goals for thriving in sex work. Flip back often and take notes. **Check in regularly.**

NOTES, FORMATS, WARNINGS & GRAPHICS

Page numbers cited in this workbook correspond with the paperback version of *Thriving*. I'll try not to repeat myself too much, just enough for context. Direct quotes will be formatted like so:

> There always have been and always will be sex professionals, at least until the invention of the sexborg.

Some exercises are intended for you to fill out **before** you're in crisis. Providing wisdom, comfort, and care to yourself when you're feeling strong can be a powerful practice to counter those times when you feel small. Some exercises are intended for **during** or **after** the fact, usually some form of self-care. You'll see exercises throughout this book marked like so:

BEFORE | DURING | AFTER   BEFORE | **DURING** | AFTER   BEFORE | DURING | **AFTER**

You'll see all kinds of graphics throughout this book. Some are just for fun, but affirmations, warnings, and reminders are where I offer my best advice. Feel free create your own.

 I deserve to live and work in safety.

 Memorize your emergency contact phone numbers.

 Does any of this belong online?

Several exercises I've read aloud, and you can listen to them for free on Soundcloud and iTunes. Look for this symbol:

MIND/BODY/EMOTIONS CHECK-IN

Throughout this workbook, I routinely prompt you to check in with yourself. A helpful self-care skill is distinguishing between the three states of being: mental, physical, and emotional.

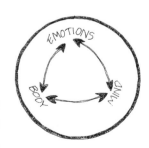

Most of us were taught to lump them together, and call that what we're "feeling," but they're not the same. They are, however, deeply interconnected. Our thoughts affect our emotions; our emotions are housed in our bodies; our bodies color our thoughts and emotions.

Most of us regularly tune parts of ourselves out. All of us, at times, use one modality to override the others. We've all encountered people in fiction or real life who are so driven by rage or ambition, they give no thought to what their bodies are telling them. Or who are so lost in thought, they're completely cut off from their emotions. Many states of suffering including depression, anxiety, illness, and grief are seated in the body; we cannot move past them using our minds alone.

A mind/body/emotions check-in accesses what we are truly experiencing, rather than what we "should" be feeling. This means listening to what our heads and guts and hearts have to say, even if it's difficult to hear. As sex workers, we run the risk of tremendous damage by shutting ourselves down. Connecting authentically to all states of being on a regular basis empowers us to protect and comfort ourselves.

A mind/body/emotions check-in doesn't need to take a lot of time. Sometimes all we need to do is draw in a conscious deep breath and then exhale. **Inhale**, taking stock of whatever script or song or phrase is running through your active mind. **Hold** your breath for one beat and name your mood in any way that is useful to you. Then, as you **exhale**, scan the active points of your body—your eye sockets, your jaw, your ribcage, your pulse. Do you notice alignment, or disconnect? Are you ignoring or overriding a certain side of yourself? If that's what's necessary to get through what you're facing in the moment, promise yourself to check back in later when it's safe to do so.

MATRIX PHRASES

We look up at the same stars, and see such different things.
GEORGE R.R. MARTIN

All day, every day on the job, we're bombarded with messages telling us *"This is how the sex industry is."* A major theme of this workbook is challenging your thoughts, feelings, and beliefs. This requires special attention to telling them apart. All too often, we have a tendency to treat these things as if they're all the same. They are not.

In linguistics, "I know," "I think," "I feel," "I believe," "I hear," and "People say," are called *matrix phrases*, defined as phrases that "designate the central situation of a sentence." This sounds esoteric but is quite straightforward: matrix phrases denote how we perceive a specific reality.

To get a grip on this concept, think back to the classic movie, *The Matrix*. The protagonist, Neo, wakes up to realize that the apartment, city, and world he thought he was occupying aren't the "real" world, but instead a virtual construct. His mind is plugged into a computer program, and his flesh-and-blood body is housed in a pod to be harvested as a human battery.

Now, to the best of my knowledge, we aren't living in pods, but that doesn't mean we don't all grapple with the distinctions between what we "know" and what we feel or believe. Many ideas we accept as truth are received wisdom. For example, we've all learned from science, from globes, from satellite footage, that the earth is a sphere. Few of us have ever independently confirmed this fact, however.

Likewise, it is possible to have strongly held beliefs that have no bearing on reality whatsoever, such as, *"Wearing my special panda hat means my team will win!"* And while emotions can have enormous impact on how we see the world, they never—not once, not ever—tell the whole story.

This graphic is designed to prompt you to consider your relationship to an idea or concept—is this something you believe? Something someone told you? Something you know for yourself firsthand? Is it always true, sometimes kinda true, or rarely true? Could this be a fear disguised as a fact?

Feel free to interpret these phrases however you wish. By all means, mix-and-match and expand the list any way you choose—they're just a jumping-off point. In this book, if you see a matrix verb that isn't working for you, cross it out, and insert your own:

"I ~~think~~ *know* RuPaul is the greatest drag queen of all time."

A FINAL WORD: THE JOURNEY AHEAD

As sex workers, our transgressions place us outside polite society, qualifying us to see the world from a different perspective. I believe sexuality and creativity come from the same place from deep within us, along with problem solving and our longing to connect with the divine.

Throughout this workbook, I challenge you to not only explain this job to yourself in ways that are beneficial to your mental health, your achievements as a sex worker, and your future goals, but as an opportunity to instruct friends and family, clients, coworkers, and the wider world about what you've learned along the way.

We all want to see a sex work world worth working in. The pathway to getting there begins with individual sex workers carving out lives of sanity and dignity for themselves, demanding better for others. We start with the dream.

Our visions begin with our desires. We write to change the world. Let us change it for the better.

Sex Work Safety 101

SO, YOU'RE A SEX WORKER...

... and you're serious about it? I salute you. Let's treat the job seriously.

The next twelve pages aren't the sexy part of this workbook. They do, however, serve as a basic employee handbook: blueprints to keep you, your money, and your identity safe; action plans to help find professional help you may need moving forward; and a contingency plan in case you are arrested.

Pretend you've just hired your best friend to do what you do. You wouldn't let any of these vital precautions slide for them, now would you? Sit down, and treat this paperwork like it's your first day on the job. Check each item off the list. Once you've finished, we'll head straight to the fun stuff.

My Sex Work Career starts here.

*Sex work for many of us is never more than a stopgap or side-gig. You deserve to thrive in sex work whether you do it for three months or thirty years. If the word "career" doesn't ring true for you, cross it out, and use your own.

SEX WORK SAFETY 101 CHECKLIST

	Done? ☑
Emergency Contact Information	☐
In Case of Emergency Exit Plans	☐
In Case Of....	☐
Phone	
Password/Fingerprint Protected	☐
Data Automatically Backed Up	☐
Freezing/Tracking App Installed	☐
Wallet/Purse	
Card Information Stored Securely	☐
Copy of Photo ID Stored Securely	☐
Keys	
Spare Set Hidden Securely	☐
Money Safety Action Plan	☐
Safety Savings Action Plan	☐
Online Safety Action Plan	☐
Professional Support Action Plan	☐
Legal Counsel Action Plan	☐
In Case of Arrest Action Plan	☐

IN CASE OF EMERGENCY CONTACT INFORMATION

Fill this out **before** you need it.

EMERGENCY CONTACT NAME(S):   **PHONE NUMBER(S):**

Fill out this card, cut it out, and stick it in your wallet or purse.

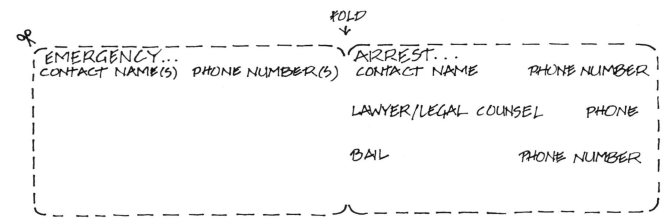

FOLD
↓

EMERGENCY...
CONTACT NAME(S)   PHONE NUMBER(S)

ARREST...
CONTACT NAME   PHONE NUMBER

LAWYER/LEGAL COUNSEL   PHONE

BAIL   PHONE NUMBER

Just in case you lose your wallet or your purse is lost in an accident...

 Memorize your emergency contact phone numbers.

IN CASE OF EMERGENCY EXIT PLANS

Fill this out **before** you need it. Imagine an urgent situation at work: a fire, a power outage, a client turns threatening. Walk through the steps in your mind to get yourself to safety.

WRITE THE STEPS OUT. Review these safety protocols once a month; revise as needed.

MY EMERGENCY PLANS

MY ESCAPE PLAN...	I KEEP THESE WEAPONS ON HAND...	TO BE USED IN CASE OF...
AT HOME		
AT WORK		
OUTCALL (hotel, other people's homes, parties, cars...)		

MY SAFETY RULES...

 When entering a new place, do a walk-through. Scout out exits, escape routes, alarms, recording devices. If anyone is there you don't expect, **LEAVE**.

IN CASE OF...

Fill this out **before** you need it. Everyone at some point loses their phone or wallet or keys—it's just a part of life. In sex work, however, these minor hassles can have huge repercussions. Nothing feels worse than knowing that we could have taken steps to prevent disaster, but didn't.

IN CASE OF: LOST SMARTPHONE

Imagine someone steals your phone. Is it locked? Is the data automatically backed up?

 Check out apps that will freeze and/or track your phone if it's lost or stolen.

> **If I lose my phone, my plan is:**

IN CASE OF: LOST KEYS

Set aside a spare set of house keys in case of emergency. They should be well hidden, but accessible 24 hours a day, 365 days a year, including weekends, holidays, and late at night. If you leave a key with a friend, what is your back-up plan if they go on vacation?

 Keep a spare car key in a safe place where you and your support team can always access it.

> **If I lose my keys, my plan is:**

IN CASE OF: LOST WALLET/PURSE

Open your wallet and pull out the cards you carry with your regularly. Below, write down information for your driver's license, credit and debit cards, bus pass, student or military ID, insurance card, etc.

Think first whether this workbook is a good place to store this information. If not, tear out this piece of paper and hide it in a secure place where you can find it again. Alternatively, there are free secure apps such as Evernote where you can safely store confidential information.

LOST!

CARD	NUMBER / NAME	CO. PHONE	WEBSITE
DRIVER'S LICENCE			
AUTO INSURANCE			
HEALTH INSURANCE			
BUS/TRAIN PASS			
CREDIT CARD			
CREDIT CARD			
DEBIT CARD			
LIBRARY CARD			
STUDENT I.D. CARD			

 Make a copy of all photo IDs you carry and hide that with your card information.

90

CUT ME OUT AND KEEP ME SOMEPLACE SAFE

MONEY SAFETY ACTION PLAN

For so many of us, money can be a big jumble, hidden in the shadows. We do ourselves a huge favor when we clearly articulate our money intentions. A written record isn't recommended, but I do want you to think systematically about how you keep your money safe at **home**, at **work**, and in **transit**.

Either: Write out your money safety protocols on a separate piece of paper, then destroy it.
Or: Explain your detailed money safety protocols to your most trusted (imaginary) assistant.

 I am committed to keeping my money SAFE.

SAFETY SAVINGS ACTION PLAN

As a sex worker, you owe it to yourself to have money set aside. Here's a simple action plan to build your rainy day fund.

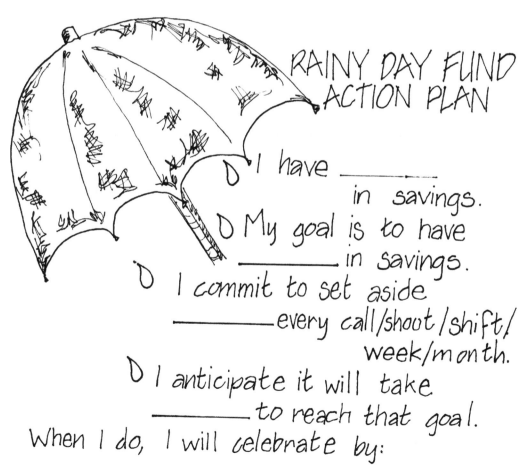

RAINY DAY FUND ACTION PLAN

◊ I have _____ in savings.
◊ My goal is to have _____ in savings.
◊ I commit to set aside _____ every call/shoot/shift/week/month.
◊ I anticipate it will take _____ to reach that goal. When I do, I will celebrate by:

ONLINE PRIVACY ACTION PLAN

As sex workers, we are especially vulnerable to online hacks, cyberstalking, doxxing, etc., so protecting our online information is critical. Check out **www.loladavina.com/legal-safety-privacy-resources/** where I list security resources, and research online safety practices, including password protection, anti-virus and malware software, encrypting sensitive information, and automated system backups.

Note: Stop and think first whether this workbook is a safe place to store online passwords.

I will research these websites:

I will ask these people for recommendations:

Write out your online safety protocols: Done? ☑

Website: ☐

Social Media: ☐

Online Ads: ☐

Email Account(s):   ☐

Online Banking: ☐

Wishlist(s):   ☐

Other: ☐

MY PROFESSIONAL SUPPORT NETWORK

I have the following people to help me become the best damned sex worker I can be. Fill me out!

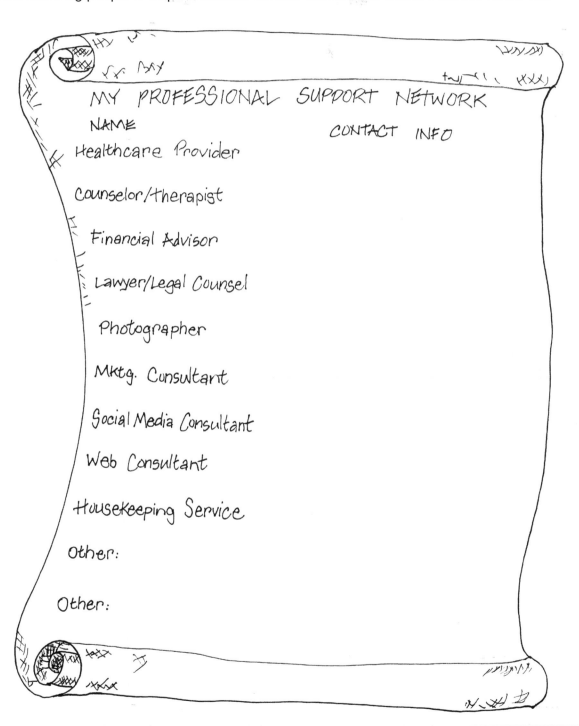

MY PROFESSIONAL SUPPORT NETWORK

NAME	CONTACT INFO
Healthcare Provider	
Counselor/Therapist	
Financial Advisor	
Lawyer/Legal Counsel	
Photographer	
Mktg. Consultant	
Social Media Consultant	
Web Consultant	
Housekeeping Service	
Other:	
Other:	

PROFESSIONAL SUPPORT NETWORK ACTION PLAN

If you need to hire a professional, here is an action plan to identify and interview potential candidates.

I will research these websites:

I will ask these people for recommendations:

Before I make a hiring decision, I will take into consideration:

☐ Cost ☐ Convenience ☐ Qualifications

☐ Recommendations ☐ Years of Experience ☐ Personal Connection

☐ Professional Demeanor ☐ Comfort with Sex Work ☐ Other

When I interview these professionals, I will ask:

I am ☐ am not ☐ going to tell them I'm a sex worker. My plan is to say:

Because:

Names and contact information of prospective candidates:

LEGAL COUNSEL ACTION PLAN

Get the help you need **before** you encounter the law. Refer to pages 36–44 in *Thriving* for suggestions for issues that might arise from sex work, and write out any questions you have for your legal counsel.

To get my questions answered, I will:

Research these websites:

Contact these people/organizations for referrals and recommendations:

IN CASE OF ARREST

Have this information ready **before** you need it. Page 278 of *Thriving* lists free online resources for advice on what to do before, during, and after arrest.

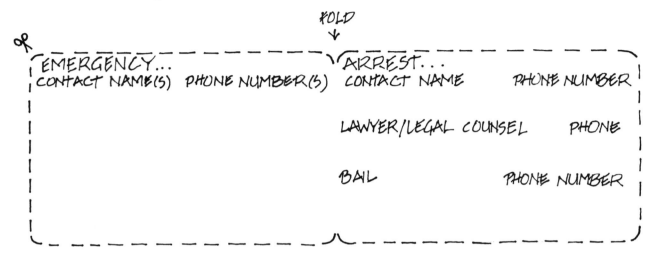

FOLD ↓

EMERGENCY...
CONTACT NAME(S)   PHONE NUMBER(S)

ARREST...
CONTACT NAME   PHONE NUMBER

LAWYER/LEGAL COUNSEL   PHONE

BAIL   PHONE NUMBER

 MEMORIZE THIS INFORMATION
In custody, you may not have access to your wallet or phone.

If arrested, my plan is:

If arrested, I will ask my support person to:

If I need bail money, my plan is:

Creating My Bright Future

CREATING MY BRIGHT FUTURE

How can we thrive in sex work if we don't know what that looks like? Here is where we envision our dream job, on the path to making it real.

Do this section **in order.** First we connect with a specific memory of when sex work was really working for us. We'll use that as a baseline, and spend some time conjuring all kinds of pleasure. If it makes you giggle, shiver, grin, or gasp, write it down—that means you've hit the good stuff. Next, we'll identify our sex work hero/ines. After all, someone right now probably has your dream sex work job. If they can do it, so can you.

We'll write our manifesto to declare what we want to see in the world, and hand out awards for jobs well done. Flush with inspiration from both inside and outside of ourselves, we'll describe with words and pictures the sex worker we want to become. We'll finish off by articulating the future we want to be headed towards.

This section is an opportunity to research, to dream, to boogie down. Try working on these exercises right before bed, and revisiting them again in the morning—call on the deep powerful engine of your creative unconscious to guide you.

My dreams begin HERE.

MY VISION QUEST

	Done? ☑
Success	☐
Pleasure	☐
My Sex Work Hero/ine	☐
My Sex Work Manifesto	☐
My Service	☐
My Sex Work Resume	☐
Sex Work Awards	☐
My Sex Work Persona(s)	☐
I'm My Own Sex Work Heroine	☐
Visit from My Future Self	☐
Happily Ever ~~After~~ NOW Begins Here	☐

SUCCESS

Not everyone enjoys sex work, and nobody enjoys it all the time. But we have every right to take pleasure in our jobs in any way we can, any way we please. Whether that pleasure is creative, erotic, spiritual, emotional, or financial—however we find it satisfying—we can always look for more of it.

It can be easy to just focus on the money or get subsumed in the sexuality, but satisfaction stems from a job well done. On this page are some questions to consider; on the next page are some suggestion words for inspiration.

Take a moment and remember an especially juicy episode on the job, where you were truly in the groove.

How did your body feel?

What were you thinking about?

Describe your emotional state.

Where and when do you feel that way in other parts of your job?

Your life?

Circle your favorite words in your favorite color.

PLEASURE

Feel free to color these in using crayons, colored pencils, or watercolors. Cross out whatever doesn't ring true for you—you won't hurt my feelings.

PLEASURE

Add whatever pleasure words, phrases, or images you love here:

PLEASURE

Pick three pleasure words and define them in ways that are most important to you. List all the places you find these qualities in your life.

_____ means:

I find it:

_____ means:

I find it:

_____ means:

I find it:

Pick three pleasure words that you want more of—LOTS more. Define them, and identify where you might find more of them.

_____ means:

I'll find more:

_____ means:

I'll find more:

_____ means:

I'll find more:

MY SEX WORK HERO/INE

Feel free to write in, draw, or paste the face of your sex work hero/ine in the heart on the next page.

My hero/ines are:

The words/movies/songs/images I associate with them are:

Their stories are important to me because:

I identify with them in the following ways:

Devote a work of art to your sex work hero/ine:

Vision board	Scrapbook	Love Letter
Playlist	Altar	Pinterest board
Poem	Tumblr page	Song

Circle your favorite words, phrases, images, and ideas associated with your hero/ine. We'll use them in your sex worker manifesto.

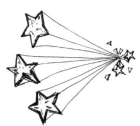

What if you emulated your hero/ine?

Keep a running list of all the times you've surprised yourself.

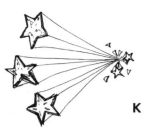

How might you celebrate your bad-assery?

Keep a running list of all the ways you might reward yourself.

MY SEX WORK MANIFESTO

Make your own sex work manifesto with the messages you want the world to know about you, your service, or the industry as a whole. Use the space below to collect words and phrases that convey your sex work ideals. Be sure to include the song snippets and attributes you associate with your hero/ine.

Blog about your manifesto, print it into stickers, or use it as your Twitter banner. For some inspiration, here's mine! I laid it out using the free graphic design website, canva.com.

MY SERVICE

Try explaining your service to someone who doesn't know you, but is interested in what you offer.

Say these words out loud:

"I am a unique and gifted sex worker.
I offer these special services and qualities to my lucky clientele."

I am especially good at:

My friends tell me I'm good at:

My clients tell me I'm good at:

Some things I don't enjoy or don't feel good at. *That's okay*. I leave them for others to excel at. Things like:

I aim to leave my clients feeling:

MY SEX WORKER RESUME

This exercise is to help tease out the skills you've honed doing this deeply interpersonal, entrepreneurial work.

A good resume is packed with two things: concrete numbers and action verbs: **Earning** $55,000 a year; **growing** a superfan social media following of 9,000 Instagram followers; **co-managing** a three-domme dungeon; **editing** 50+ videos; **marketing** four erotica books; **appearing** on three podcasts; **guest-blogging** five times.

Here are more action verbs for inspiration:
implemented, launched, oversaw, conceptualized, mentored, developed, designed, wrote, produced, collaborated, specialized, organized, hosted, supervised, motivated, interviewed, surpassed, transformed, advertised, reviewed, provided, taught, completed, improved, spearheaded.

Using your own words, what are your greatest sex work accomplishments?

What tangible milestones can you boast about?

MY SEX WORKER RESUME

Think of all the ways you've interacted with clients, coworkers, management, and civilians doing sex work.

What have you learned about yourself?

The way the world works?

How have you improved?

 I'm a bit of a badass!

MY SEX WORK TROPHY

There are many aspects of sex work that don't get recognition.

What would your sex work trophies be for?

Who deserves one?

AND THE OSCAR GOES TO...

Sooner or later, everyone in sex work deserves a Best Acting Award.

What categories would you create?

List some of your favorite performances, your own and your coworkers.

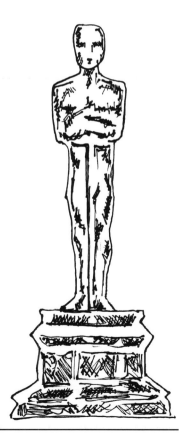

MY SEX WORK PERSONA(S)

Review pages 27–39 of this workbook. Notice what words, phrases, and ideas you use more than once. Give your work persona(s) a name, a face, a place of work, and some kick-ass descriptive words and phrases.

MY SEX WORK PERSONA(S)
Here is where you articulate the sex worker you are becoming.

Name them!

Describe where they work:

Describe how they look / walk / dress / talk:

Nickname(s):

Hashtag:

Mission statement:

Theme song:

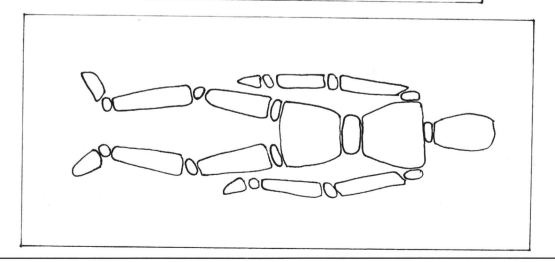

I'm my own sex work HERO/INE!

Here's space for you to paint, draw, collage, write, cut-and-paste, and/or selfie your self-portrait.

You are a sex work hero(ine) to yourself and in the world!

A VISIT FROM FUTURE ME

This lovely guided meditation is adapted from *Co-Active Coaching: New Skills for Coaching People Towards Success in Life and Business*, by Laura Whitworth. **Listen to me read this aloud at soundcloud.com/user-722400814.**

Sit in a quiet place in a comfortable chair. Close your eyes, take several deep breaths. Ground yourself in your seat. Be aware of where your weight rests in your shoulders, your buttocks, backs of your thighs, your feet.

Imagine a beam of light beginning at your belly button, running straight down through you to the center of the earth, connecting to its molten core. Name the color of this light beam. Now imagine that same beam running up through the top of your head straight up into outer space. Imagine riding that beam like an elevator up though the building you are sitting in, through the atmosphere, up into the stratosphere, so you can see the entire earth stretched out below you, the curvature of the globe.

Now, notice a second light beam next to you, a different color from the first. Give that color a name. See yourself moving to that second beam. That beam will transport you twenty years ahead, to meet your future you. Ride it back down, noticing the earth rising up to greet you. Where are you landing? Are you in a city? A forest? A desert? A residential street? Are there trees, lawns, pools, beaches, lakes, cars, flowers, animals around you?

You are visiting your future home. What kind of structure is it? An apartment building? An RV? A cabin? A cottage on a cul-de-sac?

Knock on the door. Your future self is waiting to greet you. What do you notice about this person? How do they stand? How do they move? How do they dress? As you step inside your future home, what stands out? How would you describe the furniture, the floor plan? What colors do you see? What do you smell? What do you hear? Are there other people there? Pets? Plants? Art work on the walls?

Now move to a comfortable place for the two of you to sit and talk. Ask your future self: "What do you remember most about the past twenty years?" Take a moment to listen to the answer. Then ask: "What do I need to know in order to get to where you are now? What is the first step I need to take?" Pause, and allow your future self to respond.

Now take a moment to ask your own questions. What else would you like to ask your future self?

Take a moment thank them for their help. From now on, your future self will be a resource you can conjure whenever you need wisdom, guidance, and inspiration.

Now it is time to step back onto the light beam that brought you here, and ride it up high into space, where lies the entire planet stretched out below you, and you can see the curvature of the earth. Take a breath and look around. Step onto the first light beam, and ride it back to this present moment, the here-and-now, back into your body, feeling the strength of the chair holding you up, the floor supporting the chair, and the soundness of the earth below you.

A VISIT FROM FUTURE ME

Open your eyes, stretch your body, and freewrite about your visit with your future you.

What is your future home like? What is your future work like? What is your future you like?

"What do you remember most about the past twenty years?"

"What do I need to know in order to get to where you are now?"

"What is the first step I need to take?"

Your question(s):

Your response(s):

Happily Ever ~~After~~ *now* Starts Here

Fairy tales traditionally end with the phrase, "*And then they lived happily ever after.*" When thinking about sex work, what does that phrase mean for you?

Taking Care of Business

My Clientele
Money Matters
Time Management and Motivation
Self-care, Socializing and Slowdown

TAKING CARE OF BUSINESS

We Cannot Become What We Want By Remaining What We Are.
MAX DEPREE

We've charged our batteries with some juicy deliciousness envisioning who we want to become. Now it's time to channel all of that fabulousness into the work itself.

In this next section, we'll lay down concrete building blocks to materialize that vision. Here is where we describe the contours of our dream clientele and state our money goals. We schedule our ideal working day, and name the rewards that make this hard work worthwhile. Here is where we state our intentions to tend to our bodies and minds, cultivating the support we deserve, and planning our strategies for when times get tough.

A lot of the questions here are practical, but don't hesitate to rely on your vision work to guide you. If you feel yourself getting bogged down, refer back to pages 26-44 of this workbook for inspiration. Once you've completed this section, you will have outlined your sex work business plan.

My Dream job starts here.

MY SEX WORK BUSINESS PLAN

	Done?
	☑
My Clientele	
What Do Clients Want?	☐
Current Client Assessment	☐
My Boundaries/Red Lines/Rules	☐
My Clientele Manifesto	☐
My Scripts: Coercion and Intimidation	☐
My Scripts: Safer Sex	☐
My Ideal Client/Clientele	☐
Clientele Target Goals	☐
Money Matters	☐
Money Exercises	☐
Monthly Budget	☐
Business Growth Action Plan	☐
Time Management & Motivation	
My Ideal Schedule	☐
Motivation	☐
The Big Prize	☐
Self-Care, Socializing & Slowdowns	
My Self-Care Octopus's Garden/ Space Rodeo	☐
Socializing & Support System	☐
Slowdown Action Plans	☐

WHAT DO CLIENTS WANT?

What are your thoughts? Feel free to review my theories on pages 136 through 138 in *Thriving*.

Bad clients are looking for:

Good clients are looking for:

My clients are looking for:

CURRENT CLIENTELE ASSESSMENT

In order to get where we want to go, we need a clear sense of where we stand. If you'd like to make changes to your clientele, let's first survey your current situation.

In general, I feel _____ about my clientele.

I'd describe my current clientele as:

MY CURRENT CLIENTELE

Now let's name some names.

My best clients—I want more like these:

Meh. They pay the bills:

They keep coming back, but I'm ready to move on:

I want to raise rates on, change the rules for, or otherwise retrain:

BOUNDARIES

Listen to me read this page aloud at soundcloud.com/user-722400814.

Boundaries are the limits one sets on one's behavior and others in order to maintain one's dignity and sense of self. These can be consciously stated, such as, "No sex without a condom," or, "No texts after midnight," or an unstated, internal limit that is only known once it's been breached. The sex industry profits from the myth that we're available for anything, but only by knowing and enforcing our rules can we keep ourselves healthy, protected, and sane.

So many of us were not taught how to set limits and enforce them, leaving us uncertain and undefended, which is a terrifying way to do sex work. The best book I've ever read on the subject is Dr. David Richo's *How to Be an Adult*; I cannot recommend it highly enough. Richo outlines the five necessary components of establishing clear boundaries.

1. **State your needs, wants, desires, and limits clearly.** This signals intention not only to the world, but to yourself. Learning how to assert ourselves artfully—saying what we mean, meaning what we say, while still getting what we want—is an important skillset in sex work.

2. **Nurture yourself.** Once we grow to be adults and are no longer dependent children, the only person on earth we can demand unconditional love and support from is ourselves. Everyone else—lovers, parents, friends, clients—is just gravy. Over time, recognizing and honoring what you're feeling, trusting your intuition, and caring for yourself when you are hurting builds up resiliency and self-reliance.

3. **Recognize where other people end, and you begin.** Watch what people say and do, but with detachment, without getting enmeshed in their drama. If someone does something you like, move in closer. If they're working out their issues on you, step back. Above all, don't take their crap personally.

4. **Maintain your bottom lines.** Encroachment is a huge issue in sex work. Remember: a client is a client, not a friend. A coworker is a coworker, not a lover. A friend is a friend, not a therapist. It's okay for relationships to grow and change, but consciously, and only when people have earned the right to more intimacy, trust, and privileges.

5. **Trust yourself.** Other people's opinions and experiences are just information—nothing more, nothing less. Only you can say what is right for you—no one else.

On the next two pages are characteristics of having weak and strong personal boundaries in sex work, modified from *How to Be an Adult*.

When your boundaries are weak, you:	When your boundaries are strong, you:
Are unclear in knowing or expressing your preferences.	Know what you want and state it clearly.
Ignore your unhappiness because enduring feels right or all you can expect.	Recognize both when you are happy and when you are unhappy.
Alter your plans, expectations, behaviors, or opinions to please others.	Acknowledge the needs and wants of others, but remain firmly grounded in your own needs and desires.
Do more and more for less and less in return.	Do more when you get more back. Disengage when you get less.
Accept other people's opinions as truth.	Trust your own opinions, while remaining open to other people's points of view.
Live hopefully, waiting and wishing, while not taking any steps to change.	Live optimistically, while taking active steps to make improvements.
Accept coping and surviving as normal or the best you can hope for.	Are only satisfied if you are thriving.
Have few outside interests other than working.	Have personal projects that gratify you and allow you to grow.
Excuse bad behavior.	Hold others accountable for their actions.
Are manipulated by flattery, or the promise of things that never materialize.	Recognize manipulation, and notice when people don't keep their promises.
Feel hurt and victimized, but don't let yourself get angry.	Let yourself get mad and say "Ow!", and then take steps to protect yourself.
Bend over backwards to comply and compromise.	Negotiate what you are willing to do, and disengage if the other person does not act in good faith.
Are unable to say "no."	Do only what you choose to do.
Disregard your intuition.	Trust your gut.
Mostly feel afraid and confused.	Mostly feel secure and clear.
Are enmeshed in drama that feels outside your control.	Are always aware of your choices.

When your boundaries are weak, you:	When your boundaries are strong, you:
Live a life that doesn't feel like it belongs to you and cannot be changed.	Live a life that mostly looks the way you want your life to be.
Have no deal-breakers, no red lines that cannot be crossed, allowing others to set limits.	Know what you will and will not do, and enforce your rules.
Believe you have no right to secrets or a private life.	Protect your privacy, without feeling guilty or ashamed.

What are your thoughts on your boundaries in sex work?

In your personal life?

MY RED LINES

List your red lines in sex work that cannot be crossed. List your enforcement strategies (speaking out; blocking/muting; finding a new place to work or live, etc.):

My Red Lines

If someone does this...   ...I will do this.

MY SEX WORK RULES

Everyone needs rules to live by. Below, are my most important sex work rules, which I offer as a conversation starter. **There is no one right way to do sex work.** Make a list that works for you:

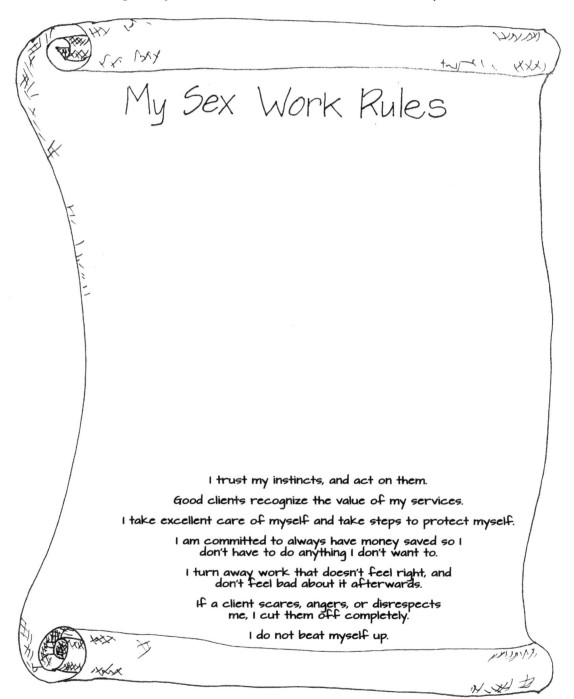

My Sex Work Rules

I trust my instincts, and act on them.

Good clients recognize the value of my services.

I take excellent care of myself and take steps to protect myself.

I am committed to always have money saved so I don't have to do anything I don't want to.

I turn away work that doesn't feel right, and don't feel bad about it afterwards.

If a client scares, angers, or disrespects me, I cut them off completely.

I do not beat myself up.

MY CLIENTELE MANIFESTO

Using positive, declarative statements, affirm what you want your clientele to be:

My Clientele Manifesto

My clients respect my boundaries.

My clients respect my fee.

My clients respect my privacy.

My clients respect my safety.

My clients respect my consent.

My clients respect my bodily integrity.

My clients respect my words.

My clients respect my personal life.

My clients respect my emotional wellbeing.

My clients respect my identity.

My clients respect my financial independence.

My clients respect ME.

COERCION & INTIMIDATION: MY SCRIPTS

Let's come up with some scripts to use if you run up against a client with an unsafe agenda.

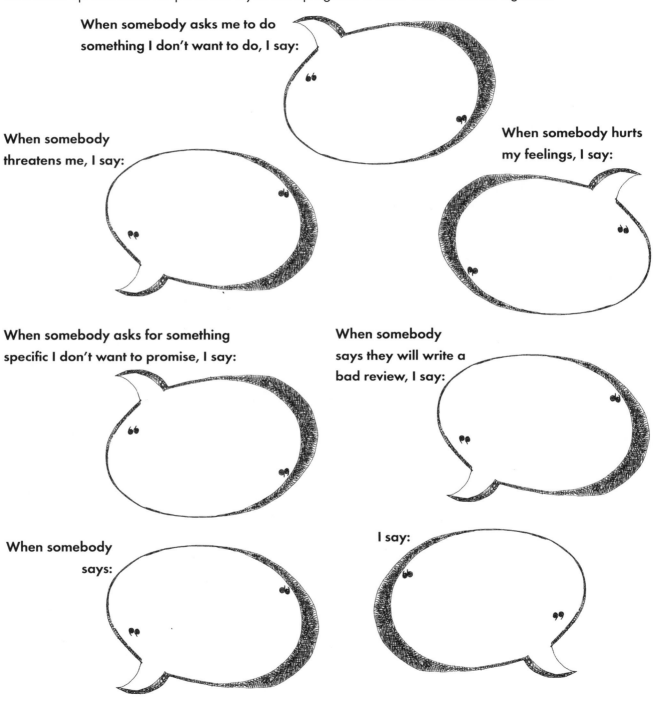

When somebody asks me to do something I don't want to do, I say:

When somebody threatens me, I say:

When somebody hurts my feelings, I say:

When somebody asks for something specific I don't want to promise, I say:

When somebody says they will write a bad review, I say:

When somebody says:

I say:

SAFER SEX

Not every job in sex work requires a safer sex plan; feel free to skip this section if it doesn't apply to you. However, if you are engaged in contact sex for a living, it is good to have a clear policy.

In my commitment to safer sex, I will:

I will not:

SAFER SEX SCRIPTS

If a client offers more money, I say:

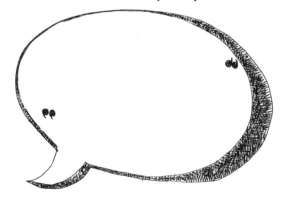

If a client threatens to leave, I say:

If a client threatens not to come back, I say:

If a client threatens to write a bad review, I say:

SAFER SEX SCRIPTS

Think back to a time when you felt pressured to do something you didn't want to do.

What was going through your mind at the time?

My response(s) today would be:

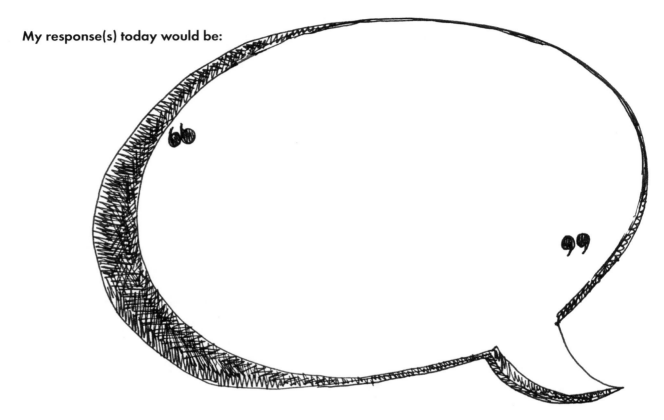

NONVERBAL SAFER SEX STRATEGIES

Not all safer sex strategies rely on words. Can you think of some nonverbal ways to enforce your safer sex strategy on the job? Here are some suggestions to get you started:

- Always carry safer sex supplies in your purse or wallet
- Have a condom open before a client comes over
- Employ an "on-me-not-in-me" strategy

My nonverbal safer sex strategies are:

MY IDEAL CLIENT EXERCISE

Close your eyes, take a few deep breaths, and imagine your perfect client, someone who stimulates your mind, body, and bank account for years to come. You may already have someone in mind, a specific person you're fond of, but for the purposes of this exercise, let's set them aside. We want to focus on broad themes, not get hung up on individuals. Try some free form writing. What is remarkable about your ideal client?

MY IDEAL CLIENTELE EXERCISE

Now let's revisit your clientele as a whole. Try to detach from any specifics, and instead, reconnect with a general feeling of wellbeing—how your body feels, your mood, your worldview.

Write about this feeling. Here are some prompts to get you started:

Well-paid	Proud	Valued	Sexy
Satisfied	Successful	Creative	Handsome
Adored	Smart	Praised	Special
Connected	Hot	Wealthy	Gorgeous

 This is what I'm working towards.

CLIENTELE TARGET GOALS

What do you want your clientele to look like 3-6-12 months from now, and beyond? Fill in the numbers and qualities you're working towards, and name the specific dates you want to achieve them by. Mark your successes off as you achieve them, and don't forget to reward yourself for all your hard work!

MY CLIENTELE TARGET GOALS

Timeframe	Goal(s)	My Reward	Done
In 3 Months Date:			
In 6 Months Date:			
In 1 Year Date:			
(Name the Date)			
(Name the Date)			

MONEY EXERCISES

The next four pages are modified from the money exercises from pages 156-159 of *Thriving*, and are designed to help connect you to your emotional relationship with money.

Close your eyes. Take a few deep breaths. Say the word **"money"** out loud.

What words, phrases, or songs come to mind?

How does that word make you feel?

What are your thoughts on the connection between money and sex?

MONEY EXERCISES

How does it feel to ask for money for your sexuality?

How does it feel to receive money for your sexuality?

Does the money you earn in sex work feel different from other money you earn? Why or why not?

Do you want to help or support other people, or is your money only for you? Why is that?

Is it okay to ask for or receive financial help from others when you need it, or is it your duty to provide for yourself? Why is that?

MONEY EXERCISES

Take a few deep breaths, and imagine you just got off work. Sitting right in front of you is the pile of cash or the paycheck you earned today.

What does this money mean right now? Write for five minutes about what this money has to say.

Once you're done, go back and look over what you've written. Do you see any outstanding words or phrases? **Circle them in your favorite color pen or crayon.**

MONEY EXERCISES

What do you need to survive?

What do you need to be happy?

What are you working towards?

How does working towards that goal feel?

What is your ideal relationship to money?

MONTHLY BUDGET

This is an expanded version of the monthly budget outlined in *Thriving,* pages 162–163. Feel free to modify this in any way most useful to you.

NECESSITIES

rent/mortgage..... $

food.................. $

utilities............. $

insurance........... $

transportation..... $

household.......... $

school.............. $

loans/credit card.. $

services............ $

biz marketing...... $

professional svcs.. $

other:_____ $

SUBTOTAL $_____

THE 10%

fun................. $

taxes............... $

savings............. $

Subtotal + the 10%.. $

x 1.2% cushion...... $

INCOME

What is the amount of your average session? _____

% that number into your monthly expenses _____

This is the # of sessions you'll need to meet your budget.

How many days per month do you work? _____

% that number into your sessions needed _____

MONTHLY BUDGET

Your budget may need some revision to come into balance with your earning capacity. Readjust as necessary.

How does this budget make you feel?

Are there changes in your spending you'd like to make, and if so, what are they?

Are there changes in your earning capacity you'd like to make, and if so, what are they?

What does earning enough money mean to you?

BUSINESS GROWTH ACTION PLAN

I would like my business to grow in the following ways:

Target Number of Clients: #   **Target Annual Earnings: $**

Some people I can talk to for advice are:

Concrete steps I will take to achieve these goals:

When I can afford it, I want to invest $_____ in:

I will set aside $_____ each week/month/year to achieve this.

At that rate, it will take _____ weeks/months/years.

Spending that money feels worth it to me because:

TIME MANAGEMENT

Consistency is key in sex work—it's how we develop a loyal clientele, making time management critical. While we may not be able to maintain a perfect schedule all the time, it helps to paint a picture of what an ideal working day looks like.

On the next page, I list some elements to a regular workday—feel free to add yours.

Make a list of your important life tasks below, then fit them into your desired timeslots.

 90% of success in anything is just showing up.

THESE GO HERE

CAFFEINE

BREAKFAST

EXERCISE

PRIMP · BATHE

TV · PAMPER

DRESS

CHILDCARE · MORE

MOVIE · PETCARE

JOURNAL

MORE

WORK · WRITE COPY

PRE-WORK ROUTINE · LUNCH

WEB PAGE UPKEEP

GET SOME FRESH AIR · RETURN CALLS · EMAIL

POST-WORK ROUTINE

RUN ERRANDS · GAMES

NAP

VOLUNTEER · HOUSEKEEP

LAUNDRY

POST TO SOCIAL MEDIA · DINNER

SOCIAL TIME

RELAX · HOBBIES

MY IDEAL SCHEDULE

CRACK of DAWN...

6 am

7 am

8 am

9 am

10 am

11 am

noon

1 pm

2 pm

3 pm

4 pm

5 pm

6 pm

7 pm

8 pm

9 pm

10 pm

11 pm

midnight

1 am

...and beyond

MOTIVATION

Healthy work habits establish good days as a baseline, what we'd like to come to expect. On those days when it's harder to get started, a routine serves as muscle memory, even when you really aren't feeling it. On the following pages, write out your ideal pre-work routine, your goals, and your promised reward for a job well done.

PRE-WORK ROUTINE

Do you get ready for work just by throwing on clothes and checking the mirror? How can you expect to get in the mood without preparation? Think about professional athletes and singers—if they don't warm up their minds and bodies, they can't achieve peak performance.

Your pre-work rituals should be sensuous and fun. Light some candles, look at porn, put on sexy music. Affirmations can help calm your body and focus your mind—here's a suggestion: *I am happy and grateful for my wonderful guests, and all the money they bring me.*

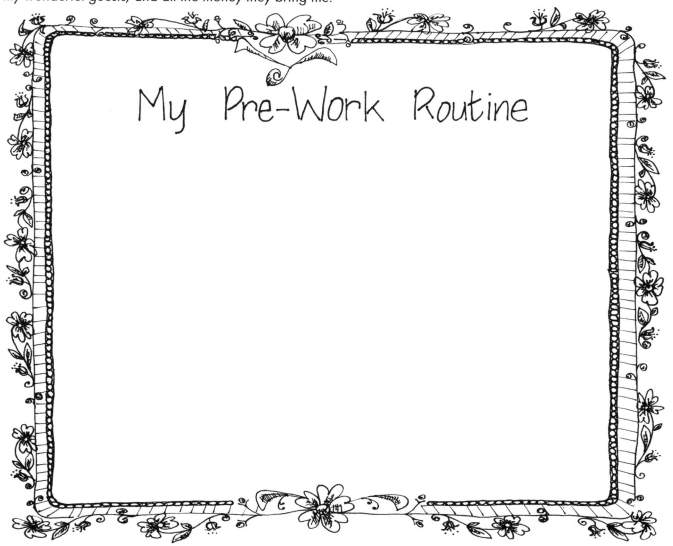

My Pre-Work Routine

MOTIVATION: SETTING GOALS

Establishing clear targets and reaching them is the best way to achieve satisfaction on the job. Set out concrete goalposts for yourself, whether it's seeing X number of clients, staying online for X number of hours, or earning X amount of money.

When you're not motivated, it's easy to say you'll work for as long as you feel like it, then quit. However, you'll feel better about the job—and yourself—when you assign yourself a task and stick with it. The reason is this: if you work only until you get bored or frustrated, that's the feeling the job will leave you with. When you persevere until you've reached your objective, sex work becomes a source of pride and achievement.

Important: Make your goals ambitious but not out of reach. If, for any reason, you don't hit them today, make a note of it, and factor that into the goals you set tomorrow.

My Goal(s) for the Day

MOTIVATION: REWARD

Have a specific treat in mind for after your shift or shoot or call. Make it juicy, whether it's chocolate, connecting with a friend, or playing video games.

The two keys to developing a good habit are consistency and reward, and they reinforce each other. The more regular and deliberate you make your routine, the more your brain connects that routine with the reward. You're not just jollying yourself along in order to get through one hard day; you're laying the groundwork for a virtuous cycle that can make you feel better about your job well into the future.

My Reward!

EXTRA CREDIT: SEX WORK SOUNDTRACKS

Mix yourself some playlists!

Songs that get me in the mood:

Songs that get me through the day:

Songs to celebrate a job well done:

THE BIG PRIZE

Sometimes we need to focus on something bigger or better than ourselves to make it through. Is there someone or something that you're working for, some larger goal, such as graduating from school, raising a child, saving money for surgery? You may not achieve it today, but you have to get through today to get where you want to go. Use the space below to visualize your end goal(s) through words, drawings, or gluing pictures from a magazine:

My big dream(s):

SELF-CARE, SUPPORT & SOCIALIZING

MY OCTOPUS'S GARDEN/OUTER-SPACE RODEO

This exercise is an opportunity to get creative with self-care reminders. Use the next page to draw a picture of your self-care garden filled with flowers and yoga-loving bumblebees, butterflies, and ladybugs. Or if you prefer, make it a kung-fu-kickin' octopus's garden, with starfish, mermaids, and seahorses. Set it on Saturn with some blueberry-fritter-chomping cowboy aliens. The goal is to connect vivid images to pleasurable, healthy activities that delight you. Make it colorful, playful, and silly, using crayons, colored pencils, magic markers, watercolors, finger paints, gold stars, and glitter. I list some sensuous suggestions below.

SNIFF ALL THE SPICES IN THE SPICERACK	TRY ZUMBA	APPLY A CUCUMBER FACIAL
TAKE A FIVE-MINUTE YOGA BREAK	GET A MASSAGE	CALL A BUDDY
LIGHT A CANDLE	WRITE A LOVE LETTER	PIN ON PINTEREST
BAKE A PIE	VOLUNTEER	DO THE CHA-CHA
DECLUTTER	PET A PET	MAKE A MIX TAPE
START A GRATITUDE JOURNAL	ROCK OUT TO MUSIC	GO OUT INTO NATURE
TAKE DEEP BREATHS	REPAINT YOUR ROOM	BOOK A STAYCATION
MASTURBATE	TAKE A LONG DRIVE WITH THE WINDOWS DOWN	HOP UP ON CAFFEINE
SIT IN THE SUN	SOAK IN THE TUB	TAKE PICTURES
LEARN HOW TO CURSE IN A NEW LANGUAGE	READ A GOOD BOOK	POLEDANCE
WATCH A SILLY MOVIE	READ A COOK BOOK	COOK SOMETHING TASTY
HELP A NEIGHBOR	MEDITATE	KNIT
PRIMP	LA-LA-LA ALONG TO OPERA	COLLAGE A VISION BOARD
PICK FLOWERS	LISTEN TO A PODCAST	DONATE OLD CLOTHES
RUN YOUR FINGERS THROUGH DRIED BEANS	SMILE AT STRANGERS	DYE YOUR HAIR
	DAB ON PERFUME	ASK FOR A COMPLIMENT
	NAP	GO TO A MEETING
	DO A MANI-PEDI SWAP WITH A FRIEND	SAVOR CHOCOLATE
		BABYSIT
		JOIN A CHOIR

SOCIALIZING & SUPPORT SYSTEM

Having a social life while doing sex work may not be a problem for you, and if so, feel free to skip this section. Many sex workers I've known, however, report that sex work impacts their social life in negative ways. Some reasons I've heard over the years: *"I need to make myself available for that last-minute call." "After a shift at the club, I'm too exhausted to do anything." "I don't always feel I can be honest talking about problems." "It's hard to coordinate schedules."*

Using your own words,

I feel that sex work impacts my social life in the following ways:

SOCIALIZING ACTION PLAN:

TIP Some people schedule a regular, set social time, just like new parents schedule date nights. It's in recognition that sometimes we need to carve out time in our calendars for the most important things in life, even if it takes the spontaneity out of it.

What changes could you make to be more available? What are some ways to be more proactive with your friends, to make the first move?

SOCIALIZING & SUPPORT SYSTEM

Thinking in broad terms, how do you like to socialize? Some suggestions to get you started:

- Teaming up with a partner(s) (doing doubles, sharing a dungeon, etc.)
- Active, loving listening (individual or group therapy; recovery meetings)
- Commiserating with fellow sex workers (sex worker support group)
- A mentor; someone to ask for advice
- A mentee; someone to offer advice
- One-on-one dates with friends (going to coffee or a movie; making dinner together)
- Non-sex work-related socializing (clubbing, parties, fitness classes, book club, hiking buddy, etc.)
- Volunteering
- Activism
- Online community
- Creative collaboration on artistic projects (joining a choir, community theater, or creative writing group)

While doing sex work, I want to socialize by:

 Here's a script to try out when someone asks you to go do something:

"Yes, I would like to very much. Thanks for asking!"

TOUGH TIMES ACTION

Let's make some promises to ourselves **now** while we're feeling healthy, connected to loved ones, and ful-filled. Write them down to remind yourself when you're feeling down:

... to reach out to:

... to say "yes" to:

BUSINESS SLOWDOWN
ACTION PLAN

It's never more important to take care of business—and ourselves—than when business is slow. Let's map out a game plan to weather those inevitable lulls, seasonal or otherwise. Start by reviewing the recommendations I offer on pages 200-202 in *Thriving*, then fill in your action plan below.

BUSINESS SLOWDOWN ACTION PLAN			
WHEN	WHY ...is it slow?...		I WILL TAKE CARE OF MY: BODY	MENTAL STATE	BUSINESS	MONEY ...by...
(time of day)			
(day(s) of week)			
(time of month)			
(time of year)			

FRIENDSHIP & FUN ACTIVITIES
DURING TOUGH TIMES

There will always be rough patches in sex work. We don't know how long they might last, but we can plan ahead. Here are mini-action plans for those inevitable tough times.

TOUGH TIMES: ACTION PLAN FOR FRIENDSHIP AND FUN				
I need help during:	How it feels:	Fun things I can do on my own:	People I can reach out to:	Fun things I can do with people:
Late at night				
Weekends				
Holidays				
Heartache, sadness				
Tight money times				
Other				

Slaying Demons

TOOLS TO SLAY DEMONS

> The toll sex work takes, the heavy lifting it requires, is **emotional**. Our job is managing stress, anxiety, anguish, loneliness, lust, and rage-other people's and our own.

Once we've set out on the road to our dream sex work career, we're likely to encounter challenges along the way. The tools in the *Slaying Demons* toolbox are there for you as problems arise.

This section offers a wide range of self-care suggestions, including expanded exercises for the five demons from *Thriving*, plus a bonus discussion on sadness. As service professionals, we can draw on the wisdom of powerful time-tested techniques to protect, soothe, and regulate ourselves. Towards that end, I offer basic instructions for mindfulness practice, metta meditation, and Cognitive Behavioral Therapy.

Work these exercises any way that's best for you. Tackle them individually as negative emotions arise, or address them once you've completed the previous sections.

MAKING FRIENDS WITH OUR FEARS

The following eight pages are intended to help resolve your worries and anxieties. Worrying is often an instinctive cover to keep us from facing true terrors. Obsessing on the size of our thighs can paper over the nasty fear of being so injured or sick we're unable to work at all.

Close your eyes, take a deep breath, and say, "I am afraid of..." out loud. Use this free-form page to list, organize, and make notes about your fears. It's fine to make drawings, scribbles, cartoons—not all feelings shape easily into words. On the next pages, we'll sort them out.

I am afraid of:

MAKING FRIENDS WITH OUR FEARS

Take out your coloring pens, pencils, or crayons, and on the previous page:

- Circle all of your imminent dangers in **red**; these we must tackle first.
- Practical fears, circle in **orange**. These need action plans.
- Unlikely fears, circle in a soothing **blue**—those we put to bed.
- "Worst Things in the World," we circle in **green**, because they hold the seeds to living the life we want to grow for ourselves.

Now classify your fears from your list:

MAKING FRIENDS WITH OUR FEARS

While we're spending time with our worries and anxieties, let's take a moment to consider how sex work contributes to them.

These fears stem directly from sex work:

Sex work makes these fears worse:

These fears I'd have no matter what I was doing to make money:

Fear Action Plans

On the next page, I provide an Action Plan page. Write out the problem, then list whom you plan to talk to about it, and where you can look for help—online, friends and found family, neighbors, management. Once you've gathered your information, write out concrete steps to resolve the situation.

Additionally, I've provided worksheets for the four kinds of fears on pages 90-93 with specific prompts to help work through your worries.

FEAR ACTION PLAN

Situation	Who I can talk to	Where I can ask for help	Plan for resolution

← priority

IMMINENT DANGERS ASSESSMENT

The danger(s) I am facing right now is:

This threat has ☐ has not ☐ happened before. If it has happened before, I dealt with it by:

It was resolved by:

Do you know someone who has faced a similar experience? Are there lessons to be learned from them, good or bad?

IMMINENT DANGER ACTION PLAN

I will discuss this situation with:

I will tell/not tell them:

Because:

My plan is:

I deserve to live and work in safety.

PRACTICAL FEARS

Pick out one of your practical fears, and try asking:

What is the worst thing that could happen?

***When* is this fear? Has this happened before? Is this fear of the future, of the unknown?**

If it has happened before, how did you respond to it?

How did it get resolved?

PRACTICAL FEARS ACTION PLAN

I will talk to these people for help:

I will ask check these resources for help:

My plan to address this problem is:

UNLIKELY FEARS

Pick out one of your unlikely fears, and try asking:

What's the worst thing that could happen?

When **is this fear? Has this happened before? Is this fear of the future, of the unknown?**

Has it ever happened to you? Yes ☐ No ☐ If yes, how did you react?

How did it get resolved?

Has this ever happened to anyone you know personally? How did they handle it?

Are there any lessons to be learned from them, good or bad?

What are some ways you keep yourself safe?

Refer to pages 120–123 of this workbook for advice on managing acute anxiety and panic attacks.

THE "WORST THINGS IN THE WORLD"

Facing your "Worst Things In The World" is really scary. Take a moment to congratulate yourself for being so brave. These deep fears have things they want to tell us—let's try to listen.

Pick out one of your "Worst Things In The World." What do you call it? Does it have a name or a shape? Put down whatever words or drawings that are useful to you.

Every "Worst Thing In The World" is the specific shape of a universal fear: poverty, injury/illness, loss of love, criticism/inadequacy, old age, death.

Using your own words, how does your "Worst Thing In The World" connect to one or more of these fear(s)? Write out any story or scenario you associate with this fear(s).

THE "WORST THING IN THE WORLD"

Imagine for a moment your Fairy Godmother appears, and with one wave of her magic wand, your "Worst Thing(s) in the World" magically vanishes. What might your life look like then?

Write out your own personal fairy tale of what happens next. Is there a moral of this story? An antidote, solution, or secret gift? Write it down, emphasizing any specific images or words that come to you. Feel free to use as many extra pages as you need!

Once upon a time...

MINDFULNESS & SEX WORK

"Mindfulness" is a term that gets tossed around a lot these days. You may be wondering why I'm including it in a book on sex work and self-care. Let me first make the standard case: There's a growing body of evidence that by practicing mindfulness, rather than reacting with aversion and avoidance, we develop our ability to accept our experiences, including painful emotions. Mindfulness practice is particularly powerful in helping us disconnect from free-form worry and avoiding anxiety episodes before they start.

Learning to just "sit with what is" can help us to:

Deal better with negative events and take pleasure in the good things in life.

Fully engage in the moment, rather than regretting the past or fearing the future.

Disengage from unhealthy attachments to markers of success or self-esteem.

Connect more deeply with others.

Reduce stress and its physiological toll, including high blood pressure, stomach upset, insomnia, hypertension, muscle strain, headaches, etc.

Alleviate some of the distress accompanying mental illness, including depression, OCD, PTSD, substance abuse, and anxiety disorders.

All this makes mindfulness sound kind of magical—it's not. But it does serve as a powerful antidote to our desire to check out, engage in black-and-white thinking, spin out stories, and escape. This is useful enough for anyone, but for sex workers especially. It helps us to establish: *This here is what's going on with* **me**. *That over there is what's going on for* **you**.

Here's why this is so crucial to our jobs: sexual interactions blur distinctions. When sexually engaged, we're figuratively (and often literally) exposed. Sex is one of the most potent ways we open up to one another, as well as understand our sense of self. As erotic creatures, we are keenly attuned to our effect on other people. Sex work as emotional labor requires tuning in, reacting to, and eliciting responses in others; money raises the stakes. Add any threat of physical danger or psychological manipulation, and it makes the situation exponentially more overpowering. No wonder sex workers are so prone to burnout and exhaustion—we need serious skills to process what we experience every day on the job.

Mindfulness practice is a bit like your cardio routine—I'm not recommending you do it at work, unless you have a safe, appropriate opportunity to do so. However, with time, you might find these techniques incorporating naturally into all facets of your life.

SELF-CARE TECHNIQUES: MINDFULNESS

I read this aloud at soundcloud.com/user-722400814.

Mindfulness is simply a form of meditation. There are many ways to practice, but all share the same goal: to achieve a state of alert, focused relaxation through paying attention to our thoughts, emotions, and sensations without judgment, allowing us to focus on the here-and-now. This method is adapted from helpguide.org/Harvard/benefits-of-mindfulness.htm.

There is no "right" amount of time to practice. Twenty minutes a day is recommended to start, but focusing on mindfulness for a few minutes throughout the day is great, too.

If you are sitting, position yourself comfortably. If you're waiting in line at a checkout stand, take a moment to orient your stance. Notice where your weight rests. Connect with your shoulders, hips, knees, feet.

Focus on an aspect of your breathing, such as the sensations of air flowing into your nostrils and out of your mouth, or your belly rising and falling. If it's helpful, say to yourself as it's happening: *"Inhale, exhale. Inhale, exhale."*

Once you've narrowed your concentration in this way, begin to widen your focus. Become aware of sounds, sensations, and your thoughts.

Meet each thought or sensation without judgment. This is key: whatever enters your mind, greet it like an unremarkable stranger on the street. Notice, then walk on by. The goal is not to get sucked into thoughts of goodness or badness, and instead, experience conscious awareness of our bodies, minds, and everything around us without reacting. If your mind starts to wander, return to your breath. Then expand your awareness outward again to your surroundings.

Some tips to keep in mind:

> **Gently redirect.** If your mind wanders into planning, daydreaming, or criticism, acknowledge where it has gone, then bring yourself back to sensations in the present.

> **Try and try again.** If you miss your intended meditation session, simply start again.

The intent of mindfulness practice is to accept whatever arises in your awareness at each moment. By practicing accepting your experience during meditation, it becomes easier to accept whatever comes your way during the rest of your day.

 Above all, mindfulness means being kind and forgiving myself.

SHAME EXERCISE

This is an excellent exercise for when you're having a good day. We can bank some of our resilience when we feel strong and dazzling, like squirrelling away nuts for winter. Matrix phrase alert!

Reread pages 48–54 in *Thriving*, and then answer these questions in your own words:

Society has taught me sex work is:

I believe sex work is:

I know sex work can be a force for good in the following ways:

STIGMA EXERCISE

Think back to a time when the stigma against sex work has negatively impacted you, such as hearing someone tell a hateful joke about strippers, or seeing a news report of a violent crime committed against a sex worker.

How did it make you feel? What did you do in response?

How would you like to feel about sex work?

How would you like the world to view sex work and sex workers?

When have you seen sex work or sex workers positively represented? How did it make you feel?

SHAME EXERCISE

Shame is the gulf between our desires and our wounds. If something has made you feel humiliated, gross, or worthless, it is important to tell the story of what actually occurred, along with what you had hoped would happen. Say, for example, a client is cruel—they show up at the door, take one look, and leave. You might say to yourself: *This person sounded so nice on the phone. I wanted them to smile when they walked in the door, and be excited to see me. I made special time for this session, and I really need the money.*

Try the somatic shame exercise on pages 55–56 in *Thriving* to check in on your body and thoughts, then write down your story—the good, the bad, and the ugly:

Is there something specific you are grieving?

Just as important as acknowledging the pain you feel right now is acknowledging your desires. Take some time to connect with the emotions you wanted to feel. Circle the ones below that speak to you or add your own:

Desirable/Sexy	Adored	Rich
Powerful	Competent	Safe
Respected	Smart	Other:

Shame tells us we're none of those things, but shame is a liar. This is an opportunity to remind ourselves of all those times when we have felt loved, safe, sexy, valued, and all the rest. Take a look at the words you circled above. Can you think of a time when you did feel that way? Write out the story of how that felt.

Revisit the responses you gave on the previous page. What do you think of them now?

 Whatever happened today–it's not the whole story.

SELF-ESTEEM

These exercises are for those days when we're feeling strong and wonderful. Store up some of that much-deserved self-love and acceptance, because heaven knows, there are always days when we don't feel so great about ourselves.

Write them all down, then write some more. ***Write until your wrist falls off.***

All the ways I feel attractive/smart/lovable:

All the people who make me feel attractive/smart/lovable:

A list of compliments I've received that I deeply feel and believe:

Make a list of things that show you at your best: great selfies, hot video clips, a glowing review, an A+ exam, a published poem or drawing, etc. Be specific. Add a little note about how these things make you feel.

Think for a moment about how it feels to be completely bottomed out and feeling terrible about yourself. What would you like your self-love mantra to be when you feel that way?

" **"**

What would you like the people who love you to say to you?

" **"**

SELF-ESTEEM EXERCISE

Refer to your answers on the previous page. No matter how terrible you're feeling right now, those positive feelings are just as real. Drink in that deliciousness—it belongs to you.

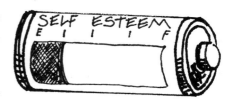

Do a body check-in. How does your body feel? What does your body want?

Food	Touch	Exercise	Rest	Pampering

Other:

Do a brain check-in. What negative thoughts or messages is your mind repeating? Care to say them out loud? To write them down?

Do an emotional check-in. How would you describe how you're feeling?

Do these feelings feel old and familiar, or new and alien? Are they part of some larger story you tell about yourself?

Try some freewriting about how you're feeling. If there's something you'd like to change about yourself, how might you go about it? How do you think your life would be different?

SELF-ACCEPTANCE EXERCISE

Follow these instructions **in order:**

1. Draw your self-portrait of your entire body in this oval mirror.

2. Name all of your body parts that are important to you, both the ones you adore and the ones you'd like to change, those that bring you pleasure, and those that bring you pain.

3. Circle your self-portrait twenty times using a pen or crayon in your favorite color, without lifting it from the paper, while saying:

4. **"I love all of me"** twenty times, slowly and deliberately.

Twenty is a lot, I know.

DO IT.

AGING IN SEX WORK

One of the most important messages we need to keep in mind when doing sex work is **we have to think for ourselves.** We cannot let society's bullshit dictate our beliefs. This is an exercise to help you distinguish between what you've been told and what you believe. Matrix phrase alert!

When I think about aging in sex work, society tells me:

When I think about aging in sex work, I see for myself:

When I think about aging in sex work, I believe:

When I think about aging in sex work, I want:

What age do you think is old in sex work? _____ Too old to do sex work? _____ Why?

What are some of the advantages you can think of seeing an older sex worker?

What are some of the advantages you can think of being an older sex worker?

SELF-CARE: COGNITIVE BEHAVIORAL THERAPY

Not everyone is a breath-and-body type. We don't all naturally gravitate to physical sensations and emotions. Some of us are brain types—we connect to the world and to ourselves through phrases or song snippets that roll through our heads, kind of like a voiceover in the movie of our lives.

For brain types, the concept of "story" is hugely important; it's how we make sense of the world. Stories structure our ideas, generate emotions, and construct the rules for the way things are, or the way we believe/think/understand they ought to be.

There is absolutely nothing wrong with story in and of itself; it's what makes us human. Where it can become damaging is when the storylines are distorted. As an example: when we believe, on some level, that sex work makes us dirty or unlovable. This can lead us to lower our expectations, beat ourselves up, and socially isolate.

If any of that sounds familiar to you, I recommend Cognitive Behavioral Therapy, or CBT. (Yeah—I know. It means that other thing, too.) CBT is a multi-pronged approach, and I'm not a therapist, so I can't convey all of it here. But at its core is the concept that by changing our thoughts, we can change our feelings and behaviors.

One technique I can recommend for sex workers is "challenging the script." (The technical term is "cognitive restructuring.") It simply means stopping yourself when you start to fixate on a story: "I'm an idiot." "All clients are assholes." "I'm too ugly to charge $XXX/hour." Rather than letting that message run through your head for hours and days, try asking some questions:

Is that always true, or only sometimes?

Is this a fact? Or a belief? Or a feeling? (Matrix Phrase Alert!)

Is this based on direct experience, or secondhand knowledge?

Is there evidence that directly contradicts this story?

The thing is, we carry around a ton of messages in sex work that often have nothing to do with our lived-in experience. There are days when we all make silly mistakes. Does that mean we're stupid? Of course not. There are clients who are profoundly fucked-up people; however, most are just regular folks, grappling with the same good and bad as everyone else.

Black-and-white thinking does not serve us in sex work. **Thinking for ourselves does.**

SELF-CARE TECHNIQUES:
CHALLENGING THE SCRIPT

Try this exercise when the hate radio in your head is turned up.

What are some of the negative messages you carry around in your head?

Pick one. Let's take it apart a little. Now is an excellent time to break out our matrix verbs. What do you know, think, feel, believe, and hear about this negative message?

Try having a conversation with this "story," as if it were a person. As you engage, notice the story's voice—who's doing the talking? Is it yours, or someone else's?

"Are you always true, or only sometimes? Are you ever true or merely a fear disguised as a fact?"

"Have I met you personally? Or did I hear about you through other people? See you in a movie? Read about you somewhere? Learn about you as a child?"

Do you have any evidence that counters this story? For example, if you're feeling dumb, have there been times in your life when you've felt smart or accomplished?

Try asking this story to justify the counterevidence:

"If you're so true, then how do you explain:_____?"

ANGER

For some of us, anger is an occasional visitor; for others, it's a perpetual presence in our lives. This exercise is intended for when you're feeling calm, to offer some insight to those days when your hair is on fire.

I get mad _____ times a week.

I consider my relationship to anger to be:

Normal	Fun	Working Against Me
Manageable	Proportionate	Necessary
Out of Control	Working for Me	Other:

Things that make me angry doing sex work:

Things that I've done or said in anger that I've regretted later in the past two weeks:

Being angry feels:

Afterwards, it feels:

Using your own words, describe your relationship to anger:

Using your own words, write a mantra or two to help disconnect you from anger.

"   **"**

ANGER EXERCISE

Something has truly pissed you off. Rage can be so blinding, it can be hard to think clearly. Let's try and learn something from this episode. It's a good time to do a body/mind/emotions check-in.

What happened? What do you think *should* have happened?

Did feeling angry help you or work against you?

How did you express your anger?

How would you have preferred to feel? How would you have preferred to act?

Was this event old and familiar, or new and unexpected? Both?

Does this situation fit an older pattern from your earlier life? Does it fit into a "story?"

Are there lessons to be learned from those earlier events that can help you resolve this situation? If so, what and how?

ANGER EXERCISE

Anger connects us to pain—either by reminding us of pain from the past, or by instilling us with fear of pain in the future. After a bout of anger, once you've had a chance to calm down, check in with your mind, body, and emotions, and try answering these questions:

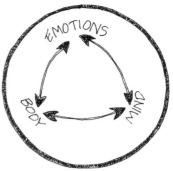

This event conjures up fear of the past ☐ the future ☐ both ☐.

Anger is almost always a front for other softer, less defended emotions, such as sadness, envy, humiliation, disappointment, helplessness. Is your anger masking some other feeling?

Describe this pain, what it feels like, where it lives in your body.

Describe the story behind it.

What are some strategies for protecting yourself better in the future?

FORGIVENESS EXERCISE

Below is a template where you can fill in the names of those who have harmed you. As you write their names, speak the forgiveness mantra out loud. (I've provided it on the following page.)

You can tear this page out of this book and shred it, beat it with a baseball bat, or set it on fire. As you do, ask for your bitterness and rage to leave you.

I ask for [the universe/ God/my higher power/ my best self] to release me from this bitterness and anger.

I acknowledge [the fear/anger/neediness] that caused them to behave as they did, as I know it in myself.

I forgive them for [their bad behavior] because I recognize that they acted from their limitations.

SELF-FORGIVENESS EXERCISE

I've provided space below for you to create your own healing heart. Get out your crayons, your magic markers, your very best glitter, and your glue. Write your name in the heart. Then, color away as you say out loud the words of the self-forgiveness prayer in any way that feels meaningful to you:

"I ask for [the universe/god/my higher power/my best self] to release me from this bitterness and anger."

"I see [the fear/anger/confusion] that caused me to behave as I did."

"I recognize, accept, and forgive myself, because I acted from my limitations."

As you do, ask for healing comfort to enter your body and mind.

METTA PRACTICE

I read this aloud at soundcloud.com/user-722400814.

Metta is a simple and sturdy meditation, practicable anytime, anywhere. It activates our own self-love, allowing us to release negative emotions, and is an especially potent antidote to anger. Once fortified, we can connect to the lovingkindness that binds us to all living things.

Traditionally, metta practice is done in phases, starting with ourselves, then radiating outward. Do as many or few of these steps as feel right to you. Sit in a comfortable and relaxed manner. Take several deep breaths with slow, long, complete exhalations. Unclutter your mind; set the day's frustrations aside. Breathe into your chest, acknowledging your belly, heart, throat, lungs, pulse.

Sitting quietly, say the following phrases out loud or in your mind. Say them as written or in your own words:

May I be happy. May I be well. May I be safe. May I be peaceful and at ease.

Allow yourself to sink into the meaning of these words. If you wish, hold an image of your face or your whole body in your mind's eye. If feelings of warmth or love arise, lean into them, inhabiting them as you repeat the phrases.

The next step is to bring conjure someone you love and are close to. Imagine their face, and speak directly to them as you wish, in your own words:

May you be happy. May you be well. May you be safe. May you be peaceful and at ease.

As you speak, sink into your intention. Continue to expand your focus. Imagine, as best you can, everyone you know, including family, friends, neighbors, and acquaintances. Say to them:

May you be happy. May you be well. May you be safe. May you be peaceful and at ease.

Next, we turn to the people we dislike or have conflict with. This can be challenging, but fortified with lovingkindness, we can recognize their suffering, and their connection to all living things. Then, the practice is to turn to strangers everywhere on every continent, all of humanity. Finally, address your loving intention to animals, plants, the entire web of life, the oceans, the earth, and the stars and galaxies beyond.

Sometimes during metta meditation anger, grief, or longing surface. This is your heart softening, revealing what you hold there. Mindfulness practice is an excellent tool in these moments. There is never any need to judge yourself for those feelings.

ENVY EXERCISE

Try answering these questions on a day when you're feeling proud and good about your life.

Who have you felt envious of in your life? What qualities do they have that you want for yourself?

Circle one quality that you especially covet. How does it feel to see it on the page?

Every pang of envy tells the story of "If Only," revealing our heart's desire. What are some of the "If Only" stories your envy inspires?

Envy can be an excellent motivator. Looking at your list of wishes, are there certain things you are willing to make changes for? Work harder for?

Not everyone has the same amount of everything, and life is unfair. What do you need to accept?

Most things we crave are illusions: desirability doesn't keep us from losing love. Money won't prevent us from dying. The lesson of envy is to look for the bounty we have in our lives. What are you grateful for?

ENVY EXERCISE: SOCIAL MEDIA ASSESSMENT

One of the most significant impacts of our Brave New Online World is there are all kinds of ways to track the seemingly perfect lives of other people. We can all use help monitoring how much time we spend online comparing ourselves to others.

My favorite sites are:

I spend _____ **minutes/hours a day there.**

I want to look at them because:

While I look at them I feel:

Afterwards I feel:

I spend   too much ☐   right amount ☐   too little ☐   time online.

I spend   too much ☐   right amount ☐   too little ☐   time on social media.

I spend   too much ☐   right amount ☐   too little ☐   time looking at screens.

I feel _____ about the time I spend online.

Here are some other activities that might make me feel happier and healthier:

SADNESS

I read this aloud at soundcloud.com/user-722400814.

In *Thriving*, I identified five demons in sex work: fear, shame, low self-esteem, anger, and envy. You may be curious why sadness didn't make that list. Sorrow, in my opinion, is a very different animal. Fear and anger, while vital to keep us safe, are states of mind we want to experience no more than absolutely necessary. Shame and low self-esteem serve no purpose whatsoever—we're a whole lot better off without them. And unless envy is kicking our butts to get us something we want, learning to accept ourselves with gratitude is a far better way to live.

The thing about sadness, though, is we experience it even in the midst of joy and satisfaction. After all, grief is our inevitable reaction to change. It's possible to wish for a life without fear, to work towards a world without injustice and cruelty, and therefore no need for anger. But a world without sadness would mean children never grow up; friends never land groovy new jobs and move away; our bodies neither age nor die. The earth would stop spinning, and seasons forever stay the same. Life under glass, with no air to breathe—we'd all be suspended in time.

Unfortunately, Western attitudes towards sadness tend to be neither healthy nor realistic. We learn that sadness is the opposite of happiness, and therefore to be avoided at all costs. We're taught there's something wrong with it, and therefore with us when we feel it. (The magnificent movie, *Inside Out*, lays out the inherent error in trying to combat sadness with forced cheerfulness.)

A more helpful outlook, I've found, is to think about sadness as an inevitable byproduct of happiness, or, at the very least, of hopefulness. Sadness occupies the space between the way the world is and the way we would like it to be. The loving response is not to override what we're experiencing, but instead, give ourselves time and space to feel what we feel. Grieving is the soul work we need to do to let go of our wishes, to accept what is.

As sex workers, we struggle all the time with the world not being the way we'd like it to be, making sadness an occupational hazard. When you're feeling down, take the time to listen to what your sorrow has to say—stuffing those feelings down or pushing them away isn't the answer.

Listen to sad music, have a long conversation with your dearly departed, or write a good-bye letter like the one I provide on page 116 of this workbook. What's important is to say goodbye to what is irretrievably lost. That's how we make room for new life in our lives.

 No matter what, my life is valuable.
No matter who I lose, I am loved.

> "This too shall pass, my beloved darling." Turns out the Nanas are always right about that.

I am feeling:

My sadness is impacting my work in the following ways:

In spite of the pain, I'm grateful for:

WORKING WHILE SAD ACTION PLAN

Do a mind-body-emotions scan, then write down concrete steps for taking care of yourself through this difficult time.

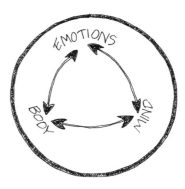

I will take care of my body by:

I will take care of my emotions and wellbeing by:

I will take care of my business by:

If you're thinking about quitting sex work:

I will wait _____ **days before making a decision.**

I will talk to _____ **before I decide.**

GOODBYE LETTER

You can use this letter anytime you need to say goodbye to something: a person, a pet, a season, a house, a city, your full head of hair, or your wrinkle-free face.

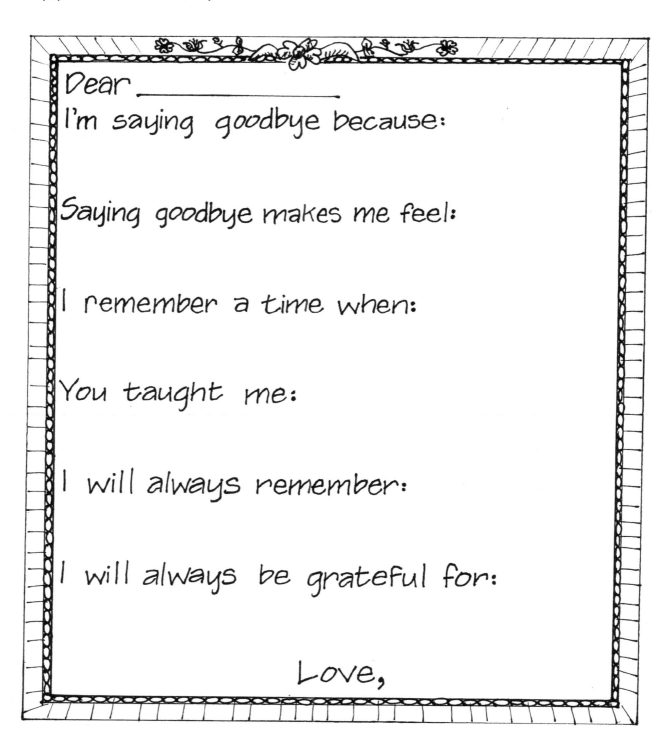

Dear _____

I'm saying goodbye because:

Saying goodbye makes me feel:

I remember a time when:

You taught me:

I will always remember:

I will always be grateful for:

Love,

Extra Help

EVERYBODY NEEDS A LITTLE EXTRA LOVE SOMETIMES...

Hopefully, you'll never need the exercises outlined in this section, but I suggest you acquaint yourself with this section just to know that help is here.

The first two exercises are intended for you to fill out ahead of time, to give yourself comfort and guidance when you're going through a rough patch. If trigger states cause you to make bad decisions, fill out the HALT + B action plan on the next page when your body feels healthy and your mind is clear. If you experience anxiety attacks, fill out your self-care action plan on page 121 on a day when you're feeling calm and grounded. I've provided some additional exercises for when you need extra help.

If you are in crisis, DO NOT HESITATE to reach out.

These hotlines are available in the U.S. and Canada 24/7/365, and are free, confidential, and anonymous, serving anyone of any gender.

National Domestic Violence Hotline (800-799-SAFE or 7233 | thehotline.org)

National Sexual Assault Hotline (800-656-4673 | rainn.org)

National Suicide Prevention Hotline (800-273-8255 | suicidepreventionlifeline.org)

Trans Lifeline (877-565-8860 | translifeline.org) Crisis hotline by and for trans* people

The Trevor Project (866-488-7386 | thetrevorproject.org) LGBTQ youth suicide hotline

TRIGGER STATES: HALT + B

This action plan is best filled out on a day when you're feeling strong and clear-minded, in anticipation of those days when you're more prone to making bad decisions.

Before you binge, drink, space out for hours online, or say "yes" to a client you don't feel right about—STOP. Do a body/mind/emotions scan to check in with how you're feeling, and follow the action plan you've outlined below.

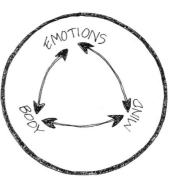

HALT+B ACTION PLAN

WHEN I GET:	MY HEALTHY ACTION PLAN:
H UNGRY	
A ANGRY	
L LONELY	
T TIRED	
B BORED	
OTHER	
OTHER	

ANXIETY AND PANIC ATTACKS: PRACTICAL ADVICE

Listen to this read aloud at soundcloud.com/user-722400814.

In our line of work, we may be treated in ways or have past histories that trigger anxiety attacks. A word, touch, or smell can evoke the memory of a traumatic episode from our past. Our mind, sensing danger, triggers a "fight or flight" response in our body: our breathing gets rapid, our thoughts become squirrelly, jumping from place to place. Maybe we feel like we can't breathe. Maybe we feel like we can't stop crying. Maybe we feel nothing at all except frozen in place.

In this state, it can be nearly impossible to make rational, well-thought-out decisions. Here are some tools you can use for calming yourself down:

First, get some fresh air. Panic attacks feed on themselves. Rapid breathing leads to hyperventilation, causing a feeling of panic. Breathing deeply will naturally calm your mind. Are you a smoker? Take yourself outside now for a puff. Are you a nature lover? Pretend for a moment that you surrounded by fragrant, exotic foliage. Concentrate on taking a deep in-breath. Hold the air in your belly. Focus on that feeling of air inside you, calming you down. Slowly release that air. The phrase, *"Smell the roses; blow out the candles"* can serve as a reminder. I want you to breathe deeply and slowly through the rest of these steps.

Next, nip off those bad thoughts. Your brain thinks it is being helpful right now—sensing danger, it's doing everything it can to help your body to escape. Take a moment to say "thank you." Tell yourself, "I know you're trying to be helpful, but it's misguided. I am safe right now, and calm." You don't need to say it out loud, but I want you to think, *"I am safe. I am calm,"* as you continue to breathe deeply.

Finally, distract yourself. Similar to the part of your reptilian brain that has triggered a panic response, your reptilian body-memory has you poised and ready to run. Your muscles need to be distracted in the same way you're distracting your mind. Give your body a little thank you for doing such a good job keeping you safe, but let it know it's not necessary. Now, I want you to gently pinch your hand between the flesh of the pinky and ring finger. Open and close your eyes. Now, look down to the right, and next to the left. (Does this sound silly? Good! It's working. It's not easy to have a sense of humor while hyperventilating.) Roll your eyeballs in a circle, and now roll them in the other direction. Hum or sing a song for a few seconds – now quickly count from one to five – and continue to hum or sing for two seconds. Hurrah! You have now completed an activity scientifically designed to distract both body and mind after a traumatic episode.

It can take some time for feelings of panic or acute anxiety to fade. **Be gentle with yourself, my Sweet Sexy.** If you can, indulge in some self-soothing activities afterwards: take a long, luxurious bubble bath while listening to soft music. Boil yourself a cup of tea. Curl up in a sunbeam or on a cozy couch and read *The Book of Joy,* by the Dalai Lama and Archbishop Desmond Tutu. Feel as fully safe and comforted as you can before addressing the world again.

MANAGING ACUTE ANXIETY

If you're struggling with chronic anxiety, try filling this out when you're feeling calm, and refer to your answers when you're having a hard time.

In the past, when these things have made me feel anxious:

These activities have calmed me down:

These people have calmed me down:

Saying these words has helped calm me down:

"   **"**

Singing these words has helped calm me down:

"   **"**

After an anxiety attack, the following activities have helped me feel better:

If I could hear one piece of advice when I'm panicking, it would be:

"   **"**

Are you experiencing a general sense of panic or dread? Yes ☐ No ☐ Not Sure ☐

Are you in immediate danger? Yes ☐ No ☐ Not Sure ☐

→ If yes or not sure, find a safe place now.

→ If no, take a deep breath. Release. And another. Release that one. *You will be ok.*

Are you facing a concrete or realistic fear? Yes ☐ No ☐ Not Sure ☐

→ If yes, make yourself an action plan that will help you conquer the fear.

→ If no, take a deep breath. Hold, and release. Concentrate on a metta practice, or try another peaceful visualization. *You will be ok.*

Describe how you are feeling. My body feels:

I'm thinking about:

Sometimes vocalizations are helpful. Say out loud...

...how you are feeling: "I feel _____."

... what you are afraid of: "I'm afraid of _____."

Now try saying out loud: *"I am stronger than my fears. I am safe now and will remain safe."*

If you have anxiety coming in waves but can't pinpoint why, this is a great time to go for a run or engage in other cardio activity. Exercise releases endorphins, your body's natural opioids, which will help to beat back those feelings of panic.

☞ I'm going to take good care of myself right now. ☜

MANAGING ACUTE ANXIETY

Here's a check-in for after a major anxiety episode, and plan for self-care.

My body feels:

My mind feels:

My post-anxiety episode self-care plan is:

    Food:

    Friends:

    Exercise:

    Meditation:

    Therapy:

SURVIVING THE BAD CALL
ACTION PLAN

Refer to the suggestions on pages 33–35 in *Thriving*. Write down your steps for self-care:

I will take care of my body by:

I will take care of my emotions by:

I will take care of myself in the future by:

List the names of people to talk to about this:

I'm going to tell them:

I am not going to tell them:

Because:

Note: You may not want to share everything with everyone. **That is your right.**

 This is tough stuff.
I did not deserve what happened to me.
I am doing the best I can to get through today.

Writing is one way to aid the healing process, helping you to get clear on what happened. There's no need to answer all the prompts if they feel too painful. No one is grading you on your responses—these are for you only. You might want to write these out on a separate piece of paper, so you can crumple it up, shred it, stab it with a kitchen knife, or burn it.

At the time, I felt:

Now, I'm feeling:

Old memories or feelings this event stirred up:

New emotions or sensations this event caused that I've never felt before:

As a result of this event, I am grieving:

This experience impacts my sex work in the following ways:

My juiciest, darkest, nastiest revenge fantasy:

MANAGING DIFFICULT CLIENT(S)

This exercise is intended to help you get clarity and develop a plan to deal with difficult clients.

Who are you having trouble with? What happened?

How do you think this person feels about themselves?

How do you think this person feels about you? About sex workers in general?

Has this person provided any direct or indirect clues to why they behave badly?

How have you managed conflict in the past?

Do you know someone who handles confrontation well you can emulate?

DIFFICULT CLIENT ACTION PLAN

I'm going to talk to _____ **about this person, and tell them:**

I am not going to tell them:

Because:

My plan to deal with this person is:

 There's no one right way to deal with difficult people.

MANAGING DIFFICULT COWORKER(S)

Most sex industry jobs lack HR departments, so you might need to tread carefully if you want to keep your job.

 While I encourage you enlist others to help determine your strategy, don't involve coworkers or management when you're upset and/or without a game plan.

Who are you having trouble with? What happened?

Do they treat everyone this way, or just you?

Can you think of some reasons why this person behaves like they do?

DIFFICULT COWORKER ACTION PLAN

Reread the sections on engagement and disengagement on pages 90 through 93 in *Thriving*, and then write out your strategy.

I'm going to talk to _____ about this, and tell them:

I am not going to tell them:

Because:

My plan to deal with this person:

 Think first—who can I talk to safely about this?

WHEN A CLIENT MAKES ME FEEL LIKE CRAP

> ### Sex work is customer service to the max, and some days it **sucks**.

Look over pages 151–153 in *Thriving*. Now, let's do a simple check-in.

My body feels:

My thoughts and feelings are:

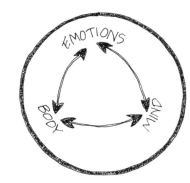

Say aloud what you're feeling:

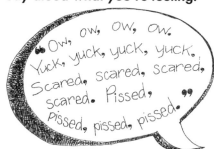

"Ow, ow, ow, ow. Yuck, yuck, yuck, yuck. Scared, scared, scared, scared. Pissed, pissed, pissed, pissed."

SELF-CARE ACTION PLAN

I will take care of my body by:

Showering/Bathing	Deep Breaths	Eating/Drinking
Walking	Loving Touch	Other:
Pampering	Exercising	

Venting (punching, kicking, screaming) _____

I'm going to talk to _____ **about this, and tell them:**

I am not going to tell them:

Because:

 I do not deserve to be treated badly EVER.

COMING OUT

If you're planning on coming out about sex work to someone, review pages 59–66 in *Thriving*, then answer the following questions:

I want to come out to this person because:

My biggest fear(s) about coming out is:

COMING OUT ACTION PLAN

When?:

I want this conversation to be private ☐

I will tell them:

I will not tell them:

Because:

Where?:

I want witnesses ☐

It's good to have a plan for self-care after the fact.

Afterwards, I will call/check in with:

Afterwards, my self-care plan is:

GETTING OUTED

If you've just found out you've been outed against your will, you need to decide how to respond. First, and most importantly, get yourself to a safe place. Notice how you're feeling **before** you act. If you're experiencing acute anxiety, look over pages 121–123 of this workbook to calm yourself before you do anything else.

Check In: Is there anything you need to be doing right this minute to protect yourself? If not, then take all the time you need to address how you are feeling and to assess the damage.

Who knows about me?

Now that this news is out, who else might know or soon find out?

I feel:

Are these feelings old and familiar, or new or strange? Are there lessons you can draw from past events that are helpful now?

GETTING OUTED ACTION PLAN

It's best to talk to a friend, ally, coworker, or buddy to get a reality check before you take action. Remember—no action is action, and may be your best move. Sometimes the best thing is to say, "I choose to do nothing," but do it actively, not out of avoidance or denial.

I am going to talk to:

I am going to tell/not tell them:

My plan is:

NOTES

Thriving in Sex Work Checklist

THRIVING IN SEX WORK CHECKLIST

Let's revisit the *Thriving in Sex Work* checklist as "I" statements. **These are yours now.** Color them in however you like. Jot down notes on what your hopes and dreams are, where you still have work to do. Notice which items feel like your natural birthright, and which feel remote or unfamiliar. Which feel easy, and which feel hard won. Some, like getting professional help, require no more than a checklist; others, like self-love and support systems, are life projects. Track your progress in all the ways that feel meaningful to you.

I love myself; I love my life.

Gratitude rules my heart. I experience little hits of joy and satisfaction and peace throughout the day. I'm not continually stuffing down negative feelings. I'm gentle with myself and don't work in a funk for months on end.

I take care of my health & have interest in physical pleasure.

I am clean and well groomed. I feel sane about food, drugs, alcohol, and my weight.
Most days and in most ways, my body craves somatic pleasure of some kind.

I have time & energy for outside interests.

I have creative spark in my life; I don't just live to make money.
I volunteer, am creative, go to school, have hobbies I love.

I have love in my life.

I make warm-bodied creatures outside of work my priority.

I have a personal support network that gets me & my decision to be a sex worker...

...and, if the time comes, my decision to get out. I can discuss my fears and irritations, my joys and successes honestly, without feeling pressured to act or speak a certain way.

I have a professional support network.

I get advice from experts who respect and understand my work and support me as a person.

My clients provide me with the money & gratification I deserve.

My clients value my unique gifts and make me feel energized and rewarded.

I understand, weigh, & make conscious decisions about the risks I take.

I've taken all necessary steps to protect myself physically, legally, emotionally, and financially.

I have a financial plan.

I manage my money according to my goals while mitigating my fears.

I choose to do sex work.

*If something doesn't feel right, I walk away. If I want to stop altogether, I can.
I have a fallback plan if, for any reason, I'm no longer able to do it.*

Sex work exceeds my expectations, & my life is better than when I started.

Most days, in most ways, erotic adventure, great clients, good money and a general sense of well-being characterize my life.

LOVING MYSELF & LIVING FULLY as a SEX WORKER is a GORGEOUS ACT OF RADICAL REBELLION.

NOTES

NOTES

NOTES

Appendix

SPECIAL THANKS & ACKNOWLEDGMENTS

Love and thanks to my Fairy Godmother
Who Makes Me Do All The Things.

To Christina & Karin
Who support me no matter what.

And to Barry & Max,
Who make everything possible.

L.D.

ABOUT THE AUTHORS

Lola Davina is the author of *Thriving in Sex Work: Heartfelt Advice for Staying Sane in the Sex Industry*, a self-help book for sex workers. She's spent more than 25 years in and around the sex industry, working as a stripper, dominatrix, porn actress, and escort. She earned an M.A. in Human Sexuality and an M.S. in Nonprofit Fundraising, is the founder of The Erotic as Power Press, and writes a self-care and wellness column for YNOTcam.com. She is currently working on a follow-up self-help book on money and sex work, and in collaboration with Felicia, producing an audiobook version of *Thriving in Sex Work* due out in late 2018.

She lives with her manpanion and dogpanion in Oakland, California.

Felicia Gotthelf is a NorCal transplant. When not cheerily putting in her 40-hour week at the San Francisco Public Library, she can be found writing, illustrating, editing, performing voice work, or otherwise finding mischief and mayhem to play in.

BIBLIOGRAPHY

While I believe reading is fun(damental), I also know that sitting back and absorbing received wisdom doesn't always lead to change-making. Learning comes alive when we're interacting, dreaming, doodling, writing, drawing, creating, and doing. A wide range of guided meditations, self-help workbooks, finance and marketing advice books, and workbooks that encourage imagination, creativity, and self-discovery inspired me while writing this.

13 Things Mentally Strong People Don't Do: Take Back Your Power, Embrace Change, Face Your Fears, and Train Your Brain for Happiness and Success, by Amy Morin

101 Alternatives to Suicide for Teens, Freaks, and Other Outlaws, by Kate Bornstein

Co-Active Coaching: New Skills for Coaching People Towards Success in Life and Business, by Laura Whitworth, et al.

Big Magic: Creative Living Beyond Fear, by Elizabeth Gilbert

Eat Mangoes Naked: Finding Pleasure Everywhere, and Dancing with the Pits!, by SARK

fail fail again fail better: wise advice for leaning into the unknown, by Pema Chödrön

Finding Your Perfect Work: The New Career Guide to Making a Living, Creating a Life, by Paul and Sarah Edwards

How To Be An Adult: A Handbook on Psychological and Spiritual Integration, by David Richo, Ph.D.

How to Meditate: A Practical Guide to Making Friends with Your Mind, by Pema Chödrön

I Am Here Now: A Creative Mindfulness Guide and Journal, by Alexandra Grey and Autumn Totten

Managing Stress: Principles and Strategies for Health and Wellbeing, by Brian Luke Seaward

My New Gender Workbook: A Step-by-Step Guide to Achieving World Peace Through Gender Anarchy and Sex Positivity, by Kate Bornstein

One! Hundred! Demons!, by Lynda Barry

Pleasure and Danger: Exploring Female Sexuality, edited by Carol Vance

Real World Mindfulness for Beginners: Navigate Daily Life One Practice at a Time, edited by Brenda Salgado

Retrain Your Brain: Cognitive Behavioral Therapy in Seven Weeks: A Workbook for Managing Depression and Anxiety, by Seth J. Gillihan, PhD.

Self-Compassion: The Proven Power of Being Kind to Yourself, by Kristin Neff, Ph.D.

The Artist's Way Workbook, by Julia Cameron

The Art of Money: A Life-Changing Guide to Financial Happiness, by Bari Tessler

The Blooming of a Lotus: Guided Meditation for Achieving the Miracle of Mindfulness, by Thích Nhât Hanh

The Body Keeps the Score: Brain, Mind, and Body in the Healing of Trauma, by Bessel van der Kolk

The Book of Joy: Lasting Happiness in a Changing World, by the Dalai Lama and Desmond Tutu

The Motley Fool Personal Finance Workbook: A Foolproof Guide to Organizing Your Cash and Building Wealth, by David and Tom Gardner

The Power of Habit: Why We Do What We Do in Life and Business, by Charles Duhigg

The PTSD Workbook: Simple, Effective Techniques for Overcoming Traumatic Stress Symptoms, 3rd Ed., by Mary Beth Williams, Ph.D., and Soili Poijula, Ph.D.

The Self-Esteem Workbook, by Glenn R. Schiraldi, Ph.D.

The Seven Habits of Highly Effective People: Powerful Lessons in Personal Change, by Stephen R. Covey

The Simple Living Guide: A Sourcebook for Less Stressful, More Joyful Living, by Janet Luhrs

The Sugar Daddy Formula: A Sugar Baby's Ultimate Guide to Finding a Wealthy Sugar Daddy, by Taylor B. Jones

The Total Money Makeover Workbook, by David Ramsey

Think Like a Stripper: Business Lessons to Build Up Your Confidence, Attract More Clients & Rule Your Market, by Erika Lyremark

Unstuck: Your Seven-Stage Journey Out of Depression, by James S. Gordon, MD

What Color is Your Parachute? 2016: A Practical Manual for Job-Hunters and Career-Changers, by Richard N. Bolles

You Are a Badass: How to Stop Doubting Your Greatness and Start Living an Awesome Life, by Jen Sincero

Made in the USA
San Bernardino, CA
12 May 2018